THE
ENTRONAUTS

Also by Piero Scanziani

THE KEY TO THE WORLD
THE FIVE CONTINENTS
FELIX
THE ADVENTURE OF MAN
THE ART OF LONGEVITY
THE ART OF YOUTH
THE ART OF HEALING
THE NEW UTILITY DOG
THE INWARD MAN
MATER MAGNA
THE WHITE BOOK
AUROBINDO
CRISTO
THE LONG ROAD TO INDIA
ON SUFISM
CHARMS, TALISMAN, GAMAHEZ
WITHIN OURSELVES
HOURS AND DAYS

THE ENTRONAUTS

Voyagers Within

PIERO SCANZIANI

eureka
Publishers of Windsor

Other titles from

eureka
Publishers of Windsor

The Adventure of Man
The White Book
By Piero Scanziani

Piero Scanziani:
A Man for Europe

A critique on the works of
Piero Scanziani by
nineteen eminent contemporary
European writers

The Swiss Bank Job
By A. S. Champ
Introduction by Roy Hattersley

BACCO: Trentino
The first in a series of books devoted to Italian
regional food and wine, the first of which is Trentino.
With wine label supplement.

First published in Great Britain in 1991 by
Eureka Publishers of Windsor
8 High Street, Windsor, Berkshire SL4 1LD

Previously published under the title
Entronauti
Elvetica, Chiasso, 1983

Translated by Linda Lappin
© 1991 Piero Scanziani
© Translation 1991 Linda Lappin

The right of Piero Scanziani to be identified as author of this work has been
asserted by him in accordance with the Copyright, Designs and Patents Act 1988.

British Library Cataloguing in Publication Data
available for this title
ISBN 1 873414 03 X

Typeset by Typesetters (Birmingham) Ltd,
and printed in Great Britain by
Billings & Sons Ltd, Worcester.

FIRST JOURNEY TO INDIA

Edoardo, the editor of an Italian illustrated magazine, is typical of his breed: neither too young nor too old – over thirty, but not quite forty. He's very good at his job, but not so good at it that he eclipses the director. He takes nothing seriously and believes in no one, but he is well aware of what his one million readers believe in.

He is a tall, lean man, with slightly stooping shoulders, who has a penchant for sporty jackets. Around the office they call him Coppi because of his faint resemblance to the famous cyclist with whom he shares the same profile and slim build, a shrewd mind, and a taste for hunting.

Now he wants an article on India and he wants me to do it. First he tries bribery.

"Let me have it, and I'll let you read your crocodile."

I shrug my shoulders, and realizing that he has missed the target, he next tries adulation.

"Give me India through your eyes."

I splutter impatiently, and so he lays his cards on the table:

"The director wants a piece on India. You are the only one who can write it and you are also my friend."

It's true, we're friends. Every now and then we have dinner together and I listen to his problems which always have something to do with women. He chooses

1

the most impossible girlfriends: too young or too virtuous or too married. He is constantly in love with someone or other, though he cares deeply for his wife. Result: endless, tangled intrigues. At the beginning I tried to give him advice, but then I stopped. Now I only say a few kind words of encouragement and that's all. Edoardo always complains when he finds himself in the middle of a problem, but he seeks out these dramatic situations, compelled by an inner destiny.

I cannot give him his article on India.

He protests, "Why not? You were in India for over a year, writing for a daily. We are a weekly, and you must have lots of notes and photos left. Why not give them to us?"

"Edoardo, I cannot. I must go back to India, I have to clear up a few things. I'm using those notes to write a book. If you want, I'll speak to the director about it. I am obsessed with this book. I'm going to put everything in it: India, China, Persia, Siam, Tokyo, New York. I'll have to travel all over the world in order to finish it."

"You want to go to New York? I'll send you there."

"You'll send me? To do what?"

"To write an article about boxing in America. You're up on that subject, aren't you?"

"And when do I have to leave?"

"As soon as you give me the piece on India."

This is blackmail, but I cannot pass up the opportunity to go to New York. Parts of my book deal with America. I protest. "Coppi, it's impossible to fight with you. You always win."

So here I am in my room, sitting in an armchair, with my typewriter on my knees. Winnie, the bulldog, is lying at my feet. He loves me, poor beast, I don't know why. Whenever I am away on a trip, he loses weight. Thus love is not a human invention.

Here I am sifting through a pile of notes taken during my first journey to India. I must shape them into an article. But journeys are always so chaotic. People and places come towards you, then pass by and leave you behind, all incoherent. Later, as you reflect on your experiences, you discover that the journey has a meaning. But does it really have meaning or is it that we give it that meaning?

The article is nearly ready: these are a few notes which I jotted down before my departure and then during the flight to India in 1965:

Rome: Thursday.
Ever since I began preparing for my trip, the phone has been ringing constantly.

"Is it true that you're going to India?"

"Yes, it's true."

"How long will you be away?"

"I don't know. A couple of months."

"Is it a business trip?"

"No, no, what sort of business?"

"So you're going there to write."

"Of course I'll write."

"Well, then, why don't you tell me exactly what you're going to do in India?"

It's difficult to answer. I have a few words inside me, but how to get them out? I cannot confess that I hope to find Diogenes and Plato there. So I answer that a newspaper is sending me, and that is enough to satisfy them, but it doesn't satisfy me.

I could say that the pull I have begun to feel towards India was in some way inspired by Jacques de Launay, someone whom I have never met and never will meet. De Launay has nothing to do with India. He is a historian, and his speciality is the First World War. He knows everything about it, he has read everything written about it, and has clarified all the premises and drawn all the possible conclusions. The other day they asked him what was the cause of that war.

"Nothing," was his reply. "No valid reasons have been found to justify the outbreak of the Great War." Then he added, resigned, "We historians must abandon the idea of understanding why. Perhaps we should make room for the meteorologists. Perhaps they could tell us whether the sunspots in August 1914. . ."

Thus the historian declared the vanity of history and its futility in explaining the actions of men. The Great War required ten million victims, and it was satisfied. That decimation served no purpose, and had no motive, and everyone knew it: the emperors, the kings, the ministers and the generals. Yet they continued to kill and to die, without reason or purpose. What could explain this? Perhaps the sunspots in August.

"All right, then," replies a friend who knows Asia well, whom I confide in while he is driving me to the airport. "All right. It's terrible, I agree, but what does the Great War have to do with your trip to India?"

It does indeed have something to do with it.

Fiumicino, Sunday.
In eight hours I'll be in India. What should I expect?

"You will have a great disappointment (says my friend). You believe that India is mysterious because you have never been there. No mysteries, but rather reality. India is skeletal hunger, tropical heat, endless dust. So why are you going?"

Why? I was in Bruges a few months ago at a conference where the topic under discussion was atomic power. At the end Bertrand Russell, the English philosopher, got up to speak – thin, withered, burdened with his ninety years. He did not speak for himself, but for us all, men and women, for the young, for those not yet born. He said that we could not trust our politicians, diplomats, or military men. History condemns them all. They led us into the First World War, and then into the Second, and they will lead us into the last. Every day we border on that possibility. We must take the power away from them and give it to the wise, for only wisdom can save us. It's either wisdom or total destruction.

Russell ended his speech and sat down. There was no applause, only a grave, interrogatory silence which echoed throughout the auditorium. If that is the way to save ourselves, how can we bring it about? How can we transfer power from those who hold it to those who deserve it? And where to find these wise men, if they still exist?

I freed myself from the weight of that silence by promising myself then and there that I would go to India.

And what would I find there? You only find what you look for. It you aren't looking for it, you pass by without seeing it.

As I walked up the ramp, I concluded: "I believe in India." And with this faith I stepped aboard the plane.

Sunday night, in flight.

I believe in India because I have already been there a hundred times. As a boy, I explored it with Kipling and we met Kim. At twenty I returned with Avalon to discover Tantric mysteries, later I made yet another trip with Guénon with his glacial certainties. At thirty I travelled between Bengal and Punjab together with Maurice Magre and Lanza del Vasto. Romain Rolland guided me to Ramakrishna in Calcutta, Osborne took me to Ramana in Arunachala, and Jean Herbert guided me to Pondicherry, to Aurobindo.

I have been travelling through India for a quarter of a century, though never moving from my room. Now it's time to go there in the flesh, and to see with my own eyes if Diogenes and Plato are still alive.

Bombay, Monday

I deplane in the pearly light of dawn. The bus takes me to a seaside hotel. I open the window wide upon the vast expanse of water. Waves wash in along a platinum shore: suddenly the sun appears.

I am overcome with enthusiasm: "This is the land of India, the ancient, eternal land; here is the sky, the sea, the dawn of the Vedas."

But suddenly the westerner within me scoffs. "But what am I saying? Earth, sky and sea are the same the world over."

Another deep thought crosses my mind. My arrival in Bombay is only the beginning. Now the search begins, the real journey. Now I must discover, among five hundred million Indians, a few men who know. They know, and thus they can help us understand. A few men, hidden from view. But where to find them?

Madras, Saturday

The search has begun, long and difficult. If I had gone to America to look for scientists instead of coming here to India to look for wise men, it would have all been downhill. Here everything is uphill. Wisdom is vertical.

In America you find the names and biographies of scientists in *Who's Who*, you find their books at the bookstore, their addresses in the telephone directory, and you can hear them discuss their ideas at the university. America is open; India is closed. Americans immediately show you whatever they cherish most (their homes, art collections, dogs, or wives) and tell you the price in dollars. The Indian values himself for what he is.

I am searching for wisdom in this difficult world, and perhaps I pass right by it, without noticing it. What is wisdom, after all? I don't know.

And yet I insist, and intend to travel throughout India, by every means of transport: on trains where everyone brings along his own bed, in the buses overflowing with families – where the children are too beautiful and too touching; in cars driving on the left-hand side (but in reality they drive down the middle, rushing towards head-on collisions, then swerving a fraction of an inch at the last moment); in the weary city buses, and in the even wearier taxis; in tricycles through the villages and in the rickshaw where the driver always says yes, yes and you never know where he is taking you; in farm carts pulled by huge, black, ponderous buffalos, so slow that you want to get down and walk. I have been walking a good deal and I have no idea what I am looking for.

I haven't found wisdom, but rather hunger.

The hunger of men and of animals, emaciation, open sores in the sun. The hunger of others penetrates my belly and twists my bowels.

I turn away, but it's useless. Hunger is everywhere.

You must find the courage to look at it.

I find this courage and begin to look at people, I learn to smile at them, however miserable they may be. They smile back and the distance between us ends. I learn to remove my sandals when I enter someone's house, the way we take off our hats. I learn to eat with my hands in a dignified manner, using a fresh leaf for a plate. I learn to lie on the ground, discovering in this an unexpected stability, a closer relationship with everything else. I learn the gesture of greeting with palms joined together, the greeting of the soul, instead of the bodily handshake, which is too coarse for this meek world. I am beginning to learn that the poverty of India is no less frightening than the satiety of the West, since satiety is an inner poverty. But what about wisdom?

"What wisdom?"

I'm speaking with the head of a major European company which has been creating industries in India for the last ten years. He repeats, "What wisdom?"

I mutter, perplexed, "I'm looking for Diogenes and Plato."

He laughs and offers me a drink.

I do not find wisdom, rather I find man. In India, all roads lead to man. In the streets of India, you meet man, more than anywhere else. You encounter him in endless numbers.

They are wandering, barefoot vendors, peasants bent over the soil in the universal gesture, families sleeping in the shade of a sandalwood tree. Human figures are never absent from the landscape. The plains, mountains, and rivers are never alone. Man is everywhere. He is always before you with his many faces, his grandeur and his misery.

In India, man is the panorama.

Kagiurao, Friday
Perhaps I have done everything wrong. Perhaps I should have tried to find out some information while still in Europe, to get hold of some addresses and some letters of introduction. I ingenuously believed that you could find wisdom on any corner of the street in India, and I presumptuously believed that the act of searching

for it made me worthy to find it.

Somebody suggests that I go to Benares, somebody else suggests the Himalayas.

I am tempted to give up and go back.

I have encountered hunger and I have encountered man.

Now instead of finding wisdom, I have found woman. The women of India are beautiful, delicate and slender, very straight due to the custom of bearing weights on their heads, very hard-working because of their poverty. They walk with a long, gliding gait, their bodies graceful and free, without the trotting of other Asian women or the wriggling of white women. They wear their raven hair in long, thick plaits, parted in the middle, an ancient fashion. They all wear saris, each with her own colour, and when you see a group of women together, they resemble a bouquet of flowers. Their mouths are pure, ignorant of lipstick; their gazes are pure, the custom of blackening their eyes with kajal is not a vanity, but protection from trachoma.

The coloured marks in the middle of their foreheads, the jewels on hands and feet, wrists, neck, arms, nose and ears are all signs of vanity, like the flowers which decorate their hair.

The women of India do not look at you. They walk intently behind their children; bearing a pitcher on their head, a basket in one hand, a small baby in the other arm, another in their womb. They do not wink or flirt or smile. In India woman's purpose in life does not revolve around her man, but around her children. This is truly wise, but it is not the wisdom I am seeking.

Kagiurao, Tuesday

The westerner who comes here is shocked. It is a celebrated temple, a place of pilgrimage, rituals, and devotion for over a thousand years, and yet to us it seems obscene.

Here the façades are covered with sculptures showing myriads of men and women entwined. The whole of human kissing, caressing, licking, grasping, gesticulating, which passion and imagination have suggested to lovers since the times of Adam and Eve are pictured here. The couples penetrate each other in the most unimaginable poses, multiplied in groups, curled up tightly together or expanded and radiating in all directions. In the immense crowd, their sexual organs lose their disgusting aspect, they lose their vegetable appearance, the woman's organ ceases to be a flaccid fruit, the man's no longer an expanded root, oozing sap and scattering seeds. They acquire a beauty which goes beyond nature; they become forms created by a cosmic power whose presence can be glimpsed beneath the marble, and which is so clearly sacred that there is nothing obscene in these sculptures.

Here love is a divine, manifest force. This is great wisdom, but I am looking for Diogenes and Plato, that is for an exemplary man, whose words have the power to persuade.

Calcutta, Thursday

In Daksineswar I encounter the example and the words of Ramakrishna. It is a marvellous place. In Calcutta the river is a great port filled with ships from all over the world, but in Daksineswar it changes completely, loses its bustling activity and becomes calm and serene.

Ramakrishna, one of the most beautiful souls who ever appeared on earth, lived here in a garden, and died here over eighty years ago. I should have been born a century earlier. I am looking for wisdom incarnate in a living man.

Arnunaciala, Wednesday

This is the hermitage of a taciturn sage, Ramana, who lived here at the foot of the red mountains which for centuries have been inhabited by hermits. It is so pervaded by their sense of peace that they say you need only pick up a stone to calm a troubled soul.

I pause in the room where Ramana expired at 8.47 on the morning of April 15, 1950. The place has not been changed since then, the page of the calendar unturned, the clock stopped.

I should have begun my search when I was young and have come here first thing. I am twenty years late.

Dera Dun, Saturday

"What wisdom?"

I am speaking with a geologist who is drilling for oil in India.

"What sort of wisdom are you looking for?"

He is an active, industrious man, very sure of his beliefs: the importance of work, and of oil. He thinks I am a bit odd, I think he is deluded.

We don't say so, of course.

I speak about Diogenes and barrels.

To my great surprise he remarks, "Do you remember what Plato said about him? He said he was a Socrates in delirium."

I didn't remember that. I would never have imagined that he read Plato, much less that he could quote him. But he further astonished me by saying:

"There's a guy up in the mountains, up above where we are working. I saw him once. He's naked. Diogenes threw away his dish, but this one has thrown away his tunic and his barrel. Would you like to go there? It's on the slopes of the Himalayas."

The slopes of the Himalayas, Friday

Three thousand metres: this is the home of giant pines, tall as bell towers, with pink trunks smelling of resin. The home of pines and streams, of little blue lizards which take me back to the craggy rocks of Capri. I felt the immense distance. A little blue lizard filled my heart with nostalgia.

I am going down to Diogenes, thanks to the help of the geologist who has loaned me a car and found me a guide, a kind and solicitous Indian. When the road comes to an end, we make our way along the inaccessible paths through the giant pines, the bubbling streams and the blue lizards.

We meet Diogenes in a clearing. He has been living here for over forty years. The people call him Dayananda. Seen from afar, he looks like a figure out of Michelangelo. He is completely naked, his long hair hangs down in tangled strings, his bushy beard is neglected. He is sitting cross-legged on a rock and is so still that he scarcely seems to be alive.

As we come closer he appears more lively and human. He is a handsome old man. His nakedness is shapely, not emaciated; his body is clean and fragrant. He opens his eyes and smiles without speaking. Perhaps he has taken a vow of silence. Then he lowers his eyelids, absorbed in some inner reality. I go near him and look at him. I do not even try to speak to him.

As I look at him, I ask myself how he has managed to live for decades at this altitude, in the snows and winter storms, without a piece of cloth to cover him, without a house; how he managed to survive the monsoons, the scarcity of food, the long fasts; how he managed to survive despite the tigers, leopards and cobras, and most especially how he managed to survive the solitude of which we die so easily.

He opens his eyes again and looks at me. I feel the intensity of his peace. Around us is a marvellous silence.

What truth does this sage of the snows possess, very like the gymnosophists who lived naked two thousand years ago along the banks of the Nile?

I look at him and he is silent, this conqueror of the Himalayas.

Madras, Tuesday

Now that Diogenes has been found, I must look for Plato.

Plato is Aurobindo. Aurobindo is buried in Pondicherry, which is located two hundred kilometres from Madras. You can get there by bus. I'll go there tomorrow.

I believe I have been formed mostly by the women I have met and by the books I have read. A hundred important women, beginning with my mother.

One hundred important books, beginning with Aurobindo. I never speak about my mother because of a sort of modesty. I feel the same modesty concerning Aurobindo and I never speak about him.

While in Rome I wanted others to think that it was Russell or de Launay who had inspired me to go to India. In reality, I am attracted to Aurobindo. Who was this man? Who was he during his lifetime, during the years 1872 – 1950? I don't know, although I have read three or four biographies. In every man there dwells an inexplicable essence.

According to his biographers, he was born in Calcutta, the son of a doctor. He was sent to England to study until the age of twenty. For the nationalists, he is a hero of the struggle for independence who experienced hunger, prison, clandestinity. For the philologists, he is a commentator on the Vedas, the Upanishads, and the Bhagavad Gita. For the philosophers he is a modern Plato. For the *literati* he is a poet of the English language, once a candidate for the Nobel prize in literature. For his disciples he is an ancient sage, a wise man, a herald.

Today his face appears on postage stamps.

This glory is justly deserved, and yet I suspect it.

Just as if they wanted to crown my father. It is an external glory which has nothing to do with the two of us. He could be unknown, condemned, rejected of men, and he would still be my father. Twenty-five years ago I read a little book by Aurobindo and was thunderstruck by it.

Tomorrow I will go to Pondicherry. I am afraid of what I will find there: perhaps an overly ornate tomb, the exaggerated veneration of his disciples, a churchy holiness. I am afraid they might tarnish the image of him that I have within.

Pondicherry, Monday

Pondicherry is a very ordinary place, with a very ordinary sea. An ex-colony of the French, the streets still bear French names, and gendarmes still wear the kepi. The inhabitants are Tamil, a race deriving from a very ancient culture – today they are a wretched people with black skin, thin curved legs, and missing teeth. Summer mist: sixty degrees in the summer, thirty in the winter, during the monsoon everything is striped with rain and oozes with moisture.

How is it that here I have found people who have come from all over the world?

I have met a Canadian – a giant man with red hair. The first time I saw him, I made up a new word: "entronaut". He was a parachutist during the war, and he has the scars to prove it. He has had an adventurous and violent life. One day, seven years ago, he ended up here, and he has never left.

I met Srimayi Pitoeff, the daughter of Georges and Ludmilla. Srimayi grew up in Paris and acted in London and Hollywood. She is blonde with pale blue eyes, a delicate face, a refined soul. She arrived here eight years ago and has never left.

I met a wiry Austrian, with dark hair and eyes. He is a judo master, a black belt by the name of Joseph. He arrived here five years ago and has never left since.

I met P.B. de Saint Hilaire, a tall, lean Frenchman with an extraordinary inner vibration.

He had just graduated from the polytechnic in Paris when he came here – that was over forty years ago and he has been here ever since.

I met Alberto, a sixty-year-old engineer from Florence, who amassed a fortune through his work in Africa and the Americas. He came here three years ago and has never left.

I met Maggie, an English writer and Satprem, a French writer; she was rich and intelligent, and lived in Cape Town, and was very much loved. He was at Buchenwald and then went to Japan. Both ended up here and have never left.

I have met people from all over: Europeans, Americans, Tibetans, Africans, Indians, all of them here, living a life of poverty, working without pay except for a minimum of food and lodging. Nearly no one reads the papers, there is no television, or radio. Love as we understand it does not exist. There are no rules, and everyone lives scattered through the city in houses, huts, or shelters. Everyone may do what he wants, but everyone wants wisdom.

To obtain it, each one of them dedicates himself to the work which aids him most in his inner journey. Some compose music, others cook, take photos, care for children, tend gardens, raise cows, administrate, teach courses at university, give Italian lessons, dance, act, participate in sports events or write poetry. However, the path towards wisdom may suddenly come to a turning point and require an outer change – the sculptor becomes a gardener. At the centre is a ninety-year-old woman, a very venerable woman called Mère.

I look at them but I cannot understand them. I admire them, but I could never imitate them.

Pondicherry, Thursday

The tomb of Aurobindo is not expecially ornate, as I had feared. It is located in the inner garden of the building where he lived. It is very simple – made of cement. It resembles a village fountain, but instead of water, there are flowers. The whole surface is covered with flowers, which are always fresh, always arranged in new ways according to their shapes and colours, the splendid flowers of India.

Here they do not say "tomb" but samadhi. We say, "Dante is buried in Ravenna." They say, "Aurobindo left his body in Pondicherry."

From dawn to night people of all ages and of all kinds gather at the samadhi. Old men with the heads of Greek philosophers, young people in a state of inner concentration, Tibetan girls, western disciples, wandering ascetics, women watering the flowers and changing them. There is nothing dead about this – rather one feels a vibrant presence.

India venerates its great men, but we do not. Here the devotion is immense, in our world, the brutality is immense. We forced Shakespeare to beg for tips, and Milton to sell his poems for a few pounds. We reduced Tasso to rags, Verlaine to begging, Cervantes to slavery, Dante to exile, Rembrandt to desperation, Vondel to starvation, Weininger to suicide. We threw the bodies of Mozart and Leopardi into a potters' field and have never found their remains. As I look at this flower-bedecked tomb, I feel myself blush.

Alberto, who has become my friend and guide, consoles me.

"Don't be sad, soon you'll have the rare opportunity and privilege of meeting Mère."

I am surprised by the fervour in his voice. I stare at him. He is sincere.

I ask him: "Who is Mère?"

"Her name is Mirra. She was born in 1878 in Paris. Fifty years ago she came to Pondicherry, and met Aurobindo. She has been here ever since. She became his other face. Let's hurry, soon she will receive you."

He made me go up the stairs, wait in an antechamber, and then go into a little room. There she was before me. Sitting all curled up, tiny, ancient.

She seemed to me a great lady, one of those queens of the Middle Ages who could heal the sick with a glance. She smiles and speaks to me, takes two flowers from a basket and hands them to me.

Her eyes are marvellous, youthful, by no means the eyes of a ninety-year-old woman. They are beyond time. She stares silently at me. I feel open before her, wide open without fear, like one of those languishing men of the Middle Ages, suffering from some illness.

Her eyes turn to gold.

Pondicherry, Saturday

Here in this village there is a secret which eludes me. I must discover it, because this secret is India, the reason I have come here.

I must understand why men and women, not only Asians but also westerners have stayed here and have never left, spontaneously giving up everything they possessed. A hypothesis comes to me – "Suppose they are happy?"

We consider happiness as something impossible. But suppose these people have found it?

Alberto tries to explain it to me with the Sanskrit word: "Ananda".

"What does that mean?"

"The Greeks called it Eudaimonia. It is Plato's self-sufficient beatitude."

"What is that?"

"It's difficult to explain. It's ineffable. There are no words to describe it."

"But what is it like?"

"How can I describe it? Joy."

Next I went to Maggie, a writer, and thus a lover of words. She says to me, "It's happiness."

"In other words?"

"No 'other words'. It's happiness."

"But what's it like?"

"It's exhilarating."

Seeing my disappointed face, she adds, "You have experienced the joys of life, haven't you? You will have noticed that they do not last. They are very brief and we quickly grow tired of them, and pass from desire to boredom. Ananda fulfils us utterly. It is perfect and unchangeable. Compared to that, what does anything else matter?"

Then I went to see the Canadian, the entronaut.

He tries to give me a thorough explanation.

"You call me an entronaut. Fine. This happiness is the ether of the inner cosmos. So then, if we fall back to earth, we lose it. Whoever has experienced it cannot live without it. Now do you see?"

I give up. Yes, I have understood: it is incomprehensible, and incommunicable.

I have no other questions, and they have no other answers. Wisdom is experimental, like science.

If you wish to know the cosmos, you must go there.

I will write a book and entitle it: *Entronauts*. I will go in search of them, wherever they may be. Because you see, these people have found happiness.

* * *

Edoardo smiles at me after having read the notes taken during my journey.

"Here's your plane ticket, Rome – New York – Rome. Are you happy? Write me a nice little piece: boxing as you see it."

"You sound like a shopkeeper – you don't have much to say but you keep on repeating the same things. India as you see it, boxing as you see it. Only the refrain changes."

He's in a good mood today so he doesn't reply. Rather, he opens a drawer and takes out a page of typescript and hands it to me.

"Here's your crocodile. You can correct it. I promised you."

Instead of a title, my name appears. The crocodile is the obituary which newspapers keep ready in the event of the death of celebrities or even regular collaborators known to their readers. This is my case, and indeed my whole existence has been reduced to the words on that page.

Edoardo insists, "You can correct it."

Correct the past? How could I? I do not read it and give it back to him.

"I find it very strange, Edoardo, that another person can sum up someone's life on a single page, but if we had to do it for ourselves we wouldn't even be able to fit it all into an encyclopedia."

JOURNEY TO AMERICA

It's crazy to argue about boxing while you are sitting in the middle of a crowd in Madison Square Garden, watching the world championship match between a white man and a black man. Yet that's exactly what Sam Gibbon is trying to get me to do. Sam is a writer, a well-known American humorist, with a blond beard à la Hemingway. He must be about thirty-five or perhaps a bit younger. He writes for a newspaper, and his editor is always sending him off somewhere. He has the hard job of making his readers laugh wherever he goes. He is complaining about this to me.

"How can you make people laugh at two guys beating the hell out of each other?"

He speaks a bit of Italian, enough to fill up the gaps in my English, and so he drags me into an argument about boxing, saying, "Two big guys punch each other in the face, stomach, and liver, smash each other's cheekbones and foreheads till the blood pours out of their mouths, their noses, and their eyes, in hopes that the other will soon collapse unconscious, or perhaps even die."

I have flown across the Atlantic just to watch these two men break each other's jaws, and you expect me to tell you you're right, Sam? I enjoy boxing. I have done some myself, and I do not intend to justify my enjoyment of this sport, though it wouldn't be too difficult. We are all fighters, Sam. Even you battle with your boss. If you don't fight back, you don't survive. Have you ever been in the ring, Sam, face to face with your opponent, with those gloves on your fists? Without courage and brains, you're lost.

This is the ancient struggle, the primeval combat which shaped us. If you deny this fact, then you understand nothing about man.

"Look at that!" he shouts pointing as a gumshield flies out of the mouth of the black contender and lands on the ground. For a moment Sam thought that the poor man had lost his real choppers. He whispers in my ear as the bell sounds, "Twenty hundred years of Christianity . . . "

I splutter impatiently. Twenty centuries of Christianity, twenty-five of Judaism, twelve of Islam, thirty of Buddhism, forty of Hinduism. So what? We Christians have excelled in slaughtering each other for nearly two thousand years. Rather we take the prize – killing people with a sword used to be hard work, after thirty victims including men, women, and children, the good Christian murderer was completely worn out. Now you can kill millions just by pushing a button. It has become effortless.

"You know what, Sam, not only do I like boxing, I also like cockfighting. I remember once, in the Canary Islands . . . "

"Oh, no," he groans, and an expression of horror spreads across his face. He looks away.

"Don't look at me like that, Sam. Have you ever asked the rooster his opinion? Do you know how they killed the chicken you are digesting at this very moment? They twisted his neck (our cervical arthrosis is nothing in comparison) a couple of times, and then slit his throat with a knife, and drained his blood out drop by drop, as he lay dying. On the other hand, the rooster is much better off totally involved in the battle, suddenly killed by his rival with a single blow."

Sam avoids looking at me, and murmurs in disgust, "And you write about saints and sages."

Sam, you chicken-eater, you are distracting me from the match and ruining my fun. Another bell sounds. Yes, it's true. I often write about saints and sages. Who struggles more than they do? Saints battle the powers of evil, and sages struggle against human stupidity: your stupidity and also my own. So let's confess our stupidity.

He laughs and gives me a slap on the back. Strong and athletic as he is, it's a wonder he doesn't dislocate my shoulder. The force of the blow shoves me into the lap of my neighbour, and Sam introduces me to her, Essy Mills, society columnist – she knows everything about everyone. Long, black, straight hair, an unusual face, mixed ancestry perhaps: tan skin, a large mouth, but a charming little nose. Tall, slender, enchanting. She greets me in French.

Who would have ever thought that it is precisely here, in this place, that I would find the justification for my desire to come to America; here below the ring, my search has begun, my search and my encounters. Whoever would have thought that everything would begin here while this black man and this white man are thrashing it out, while the crowd is screaming wildly, while Sam is looking in the other direction and Essy is uttering little cries of excitement. The future is always ahead of us, invisible. It casts its shadow at our feet, unseen.

Why can't we see the future? We can see nearly everything else. With infra-red rays we can see in pitch blackness. With a telescope we may observe the distant galaxy, Andromeda. Television enables us to see what is happening on the other side of the globe, via satellite. But not the future – it's there, just a fraction of an inch in front of our nose, and yet we cannot see it. Behind that veil everything is black.

But perhaps tonight a miracle may happen. Tonight, I may be able to break through the wall of the future and discover what is going to happen a half-hour ahead of time. Not all of tomorrow, nor all of next week, nor the coming month or year. Only what is going to happen in half an hour's time, and to be the only person to know it in advance.

To know, for example, that Sam's plan to take the midnight flight to California will end in nothing. In half an hour, he will abandon this idea. To know that our Argentinian colleague's efforts to invite Essy to a nightclub later are all in vain. She will come with us to a restaurant. To know how the match will end: that on the eighth round the black opponent will collapse in the ring.

At that point, everything becomes so absurd. It's absurd to rush to the loser's corner, to give him advice, massage him, and encourage him. During the eighth round he will fall. The other's desperation as he lies in his corner, seemingly done for, is equally absurd. After all, during the eighth round he will win.

And I am absurd too, I know which of the two will be the new champion, and here I am sitting here grinning, when I should be gathering all the money in my pocket together, getting everyone – Sam, Essy, and maybe even our Argentinian colleague – to lend me some more, or even rushing off to the hotel to get the rest and then hurrying back to Madison Square Garden before the eighth round, asking everyone where the bookmakers are, just as the seventh round is ending. But no one knows where they are, so I finally ask a policeman.

"A bookmaker! A bookmaker!"

"A bookmaker?" asks the policeman indignantly. The referee is counting to ten while the guard takes me outside. In the United States betting is a crime. The half-hour has ended.

After the match, Sam really did change his mind about the flight, and Essy did not accept the Argentinian's invitation. Those were easy predictions. But instead, the black man won. In the wee hours of the morning, we are eating huge steaks in a restaurant on Broadway. Between mouthfuls of steak and sips of beer, we talk: Essy in French, Sam in Italian. I listen silently. Not only because my English is inadequate, but also because of my disappointment over the loss of my favourite. Now that the fight is over, I choose the path of non-violence, which is also innocence: do not harm.

At this thought, I find myself in India, the homeland of Gandhi, the master of innocence. Back in India, to 1965. Since that moment, innocence has followed me, a shadow, a refrain, a form of nostalgia. India and the entronauts. My mind flashes back to the place and the circumstances in which I coined that word, "entronauts".

"Sam, you're right. Let's look to the sages, not to the boxers. Let's look to the entronauts."

He doesn't understand and stares at me, perplexed as he swallows a piece of steak and takes a sip of beer. Bits of foam cling to his beard and moustache.

"Entronauts?"

I try to explain as best I can. I begin at the beginning, beginning with the problem of death. Well

(I say) we all die, everyone always dies and no one has ever escaped this fate. Barnard has tried, by transplanting hearts. I mean, you're here, and you rush about left and right, you have very few pleasures and a lot of problems. In the end you die, like your father, your grandfather, your great-grandfather, and all the others before you. Everybody, even you, Essy, fair maid with a hint of mixed blood, and you too, Sam, so gentle and polite, so athletic and Christian. And so will I, before the two of you, because I am older.

Essy, very kindly, says, "You old? No. *Quand on est jeune on l'est pour la vie . . .* "

A kind but useless remark. Useless the protestations of the young. After all these millennia, what good has man's long protest against death done?

But then we have the entronauts. Do you know what entronautics is? I discovered it in India, but it also exists elsewhere. I want to go everywhere, wherever there are entronauts: I have news of them in Paris, Lebanon, Persia, from other places in India, Tibet, Japan, China, and Mt. Athos. I want to go everywhere. There is a technique, you see. A technique to become immortal. And in America? Perhaps even in America.

They are silent. Then Essy says rather coldly, "And never die? To be fifty years old, then eighty, then a hundred, and keep on growing more and more decrepit? No thanks."

How hard it is to explain, at this early hour of the morning after a boxing match while eating steak and drinking beer. But I must try to explain, not for them, but for myself. So as not to be the orphan of my certainties.

Sam, stroking his beard, says, "What is certainty?"

No, Sam, here I've got you. Certainty is an experience. You know exactly what sugar is like when you have tasted it.

Cosmonautics, entronautics, from the former, the latter derived.

Cosmonautics, full of mystery. First: gravity. More than two centuries after Newton and we still know nothing. What is its nature? We know how fast light travels and we know that opaque bodies arrest it, that prisms break it down, and that lenses deflect it. But gravity exists independently of other circumstances. It eludes the physical and chemical conditions of bodies, and yet it dominates them: invisible, inaudible, and intangible. We experience it as weight, and that is all, and yet it is gravity which sustains the movement of the stars and the orbits of the heavens. A mystery.

Cosmonautics, full of fantasy. Perhaps a cosmonaut will journey at the speed of light to Andromeda, and then return. It will take him the time span of fifty years. But in the meantime, four million years will have elapsed on earth. Fantastic!

Entronauts, full of mystery. Entronauts do not look towards the outside, they look in, and study how we are made. Aside from our body, we also have a psyche which is continually lit and coloured by the impulses of attraction and dislike, joy and boredom, by deep emotions such as love or horror, by the desire for power, the desire to posses, to escape, to die. Aside from our body, we have a mind dense with thoughts, which is ceaselessly formulating ideas, moving back between past and future, an endless stream of words, movements, illumination. Mystery.

Entronautics, full of fantasy. Apart from our psyche, our mind dwells in a hidden, blessed place: after a long journey, the voyager may reach the inner Andromeda.

There the years do not pass, and death does not exist. Fantastic!

Have you never noticed that the most important things are invisible? The human soul and universal gravity.

Essy, re-applying her lipstick, "I don't like to talk about the soul, because you always end up talking about God. Aren't you tired of that old word?"

Sam, lighting his pipe. "We're tired. Let's go get some sleep."

We all try to get some rest. Easy for them, but not for me, because of jet lag. I am not sure where those time zones are located, but someone inside me knows very well. He knows so well that he doesn't want to sleep, because yesterday I was in Europe in another time zone. Someone inside me hasn't taken note of my transatlantic flight. He thinks he is still in Rome. It seems that the same thing happens to plants. I have been reduced to the obtuseness of the vegetable world.

I try television, ever present in every hotel room. When I am in Milan or Zurich, the television always has a hypnotic effect on me. I sit in an armchair, and after watching a few minutes of television, I doze off, though not intentionally. Here I lie in bed, craving sleep but wide awake due to an old Mrs. Miniver film continually interrupted by commercials. Worn out and bleary-eyed, I stare at the familiar scenes: they are about to kiss (commercial), they are about to leave each other (commercial) they are about to die (commercial). Dawn streams in through the window.

Sam comes to the hotel. "Your entronauts must be mad, as mad as you are. Wherever did you find them?"

I told you last night. In India, at the mouth of the Ganges, in Pondicherry, in the red mountains. I have heard about others and I know where to find them. There's a group of out-of-the-body seekers in Paris, and near Madras, there's a whole city of entronauts. I've also heard about special monasteries in Japan and on Mt. Athos. In America? Perhaps, also in America. That's why I have come here.

He pulls at a hair of his blond beard.

"What do you know about our monasteries? Our American, secular monasteries. I know one in California with twenty sages. I'll take you there. Why don't you come with me to California?"

"Sages?"

"Sages."

We spend the afternoon in Manhattan, the place where the power of western man is most obvious. Many Americans despise Manhattan and its continual growth of short-lived skyscrapers. Edmund Wilson once wrote that he wouldn't mind if it was all destroyed by an atomic explosion, along with Moscow and those sad, Russian bureaucratic office buildings. But I love Manhattan. Everything and everyone can be found here, a cross-section of the twentieth century.

Here, it is today, whereas elsewhere it is still yesterday.

Yet in Manhattan, man is unhappy. You meet gloomy faces everywhere, black and white. Many people talk to themselves. When you talk to yourself, it is always a dialogue, and you always feels uneasy with the interlocutor. Perhaps the men and women of Manhattan know that they are the hostages of Moscow's nuclear power, just as the men and women of Moscow know that they are the hostages of American nuclear power.

Historians have calculated that one hundred and fifty thousand wars have occurred over the last five thousand years. Yet we claim that man wants peace. As long as he remains in his present state, war will be indispensable to him. Only through a process of spiritualization will war become useless.

The unhappiness of man today is very widespread. It is not limited to New York. It is the unhappiness of our century: Moscow, Paris, Prague, London, Rome, an unhappiness against which the best of our youth protest.

They say, "No, no" and offer you a flower. You look at them and do not understand them.

But do you understand yourself? We do not understand ourselves, nor our parents, or grandparents, and yet we are their children, though very different from them.

We have lost the alternating of day and night, we are unaware of dawn or sunset. We have lost the changing of the seasons. We live in greenhouses with conditioned temperatures. We have polluted food, water, and air; we have multiplied disease and anxiety. We obstruct births or artificially provoke them. We have lost the distance between the places of the earth. Earning money which was once the means to satisfy our needs has become the sole aim of our existence. Thus we have also lost the joy of work and are compelled to work harder and harder to earn more and more money. But what good does a higher salary do us if it chains us to the assembly line and the bureaucracy? They take our lives in exchange for the money they give us, and leave us empty and alone, our backs bent to the ground.

Sam smiles between his beard and moustache.

"Isn't a good standard of living enough for you? It's enough for me."

"Standard of living?" As if we were a herd of cattle.

On the plane they are always serving you food: breakfast, cocktails, lunch, snacks, drinks, dinner, candy, from departure to arrival. This is not done out of hospitality, politeness, or competition with other airlines. It's done to keep us under control.

They have realized that eating lessens fear. To varying degrees, everyone is afraid in aeroplanes.

Even those who are not afraid will begin to feel fear at the slightest creaking of the plane. Fear is tension, and when we eat, we relax. If you are afraid, you cannot eat and if you can eat, you are not afraid.

It would mean trouble if people began to be frightened, if they were to get out of their seats and start shouting. So when the air hostesses aren't stuffing things down our throats, they keep us tied up. As soon as the plane begins to jump, a sign lights up and a voice announces:

"Please fasten your seat belts, thank you."

The seat belt is quite useless in a collision at one thousand kilometres an hour. They'd even be useless in a car, being so loose, and so low around the body.

But they keep everyone in his place. Immobile and dignified, even in the worst circumstances, and that is quite right, because dignity is always necessary, especially in dying.

This is what Sam, the macabre humorist, is explaining to me as we descend into Los Angeles airport. He laughs heartily and I wonder what his face would look like without the beard and moustache.

Here I am in California, alas, with more accumulated jet lag.

Sam is driving us in the car which will take us from

Los Angeles to the lay monastery. We drive through the city without ever encountering the city itself. The centre is a knot of highways, parking lots, and garages. All the rest is the suburbs, stretching on for hundreds and hundreds of miles: houses, villas, markets, verandas, towers, cottages, the whole of Lombardy could fit into this space.

Sam describes Los Angeles to me. The city is inhabited by Manmobiles (the neologism isn't very nice, but it's to the point), very recent creatures. There are over seven million of them, and the population is on the increase. The manmobile resembles the centaur of the days of horses. Man is attached to his automobile and vice versa. There are a few isolated cars and a few isolated pedestrians, aborigines well on the way to extinction.

The manmobile is a four-wheeled creature, with an outer body which serves both as a garment indicating status and as a permanent home. It is often equipped with: air conditioner, telephone, tape recorder, video, radio, stereo, fridge with ice, drinks, and food; typewriter; razor; shower; drawers containing everything needed for personal toiletry, first aid, and medicine; seats which fold out into tables and chairs; bed for resting or making love; sheets and blankets, in other words, a home the likes of which few men on earth enjoy, the home of a lifetime, and according to the statistics, a tomb for one's death.

Amid all this perfection, the only defect of the manmobile is that it leaves a trail of gas behind it, a silent though at times explosive gas which is very harmful. This bluish smog is fatal to plants, grass, birds, dogs, and cats, and also to human beings who suffer from headaches, anaemia, ulcers, and tumours. So Los Angeles is also equipped with magnificent hospitals.

As we drive through the centre, we have to keep handkerchiefs in front of our noses. The few pedestrians are all wearing surgeons' masks. Ten years from now, Los Angeles will be the largest city in the world. Not only that, it will be the model for the future.

We are near the lay monastery. There are others in the area, but Sam preferred the smaller one, with only twenty sages.

"Sages?"

"Sages – not madmen like your entronauts. Here we are."

At first sight I don't like the looks of these sages, and I wonder if my trip to the United States hasn't been a waste of time. One stutters, another bites his nails, the third has a nervous tic, the fourth has a disgusted expression, the fifth is very effeminate, the sixth is extremely smug.

Sam, what did you mean by "sages"? They are all very cultured, possess an encyclopedic knowledge, speak several languages, and are very interesting people; a couple are quite likeable. But wisdom is something else. It isn't simply knowledge, but the ability to comprehend experience. Wisdom is an inner exploration, a way of life, a spiritual quality. Let's not confuse wool with silk, Sam. Wool grows on sheep, but the silkworm extracts silk from within itself before it changes into a moth.

The monastery exists – secular, scientific, hygienic, and not only in California. There must be a dozen of them in beautiful places with lovely Spanish names: Palo Alto, La Jolla, Santa Barbara, Santa Monica. White villas, in moorish, classical, or futuristic style, all comfortable and opulent: shaded arcades, orange groves, beaches. Villas designed to host thinkers, and thus called THINK TANKS.

Americans are explicit when they describe. Explicit and numerical. Sam knows and explains. Americans are nationalists, like everyone else, like the Russians, Chinese, Czechs, Arabs, even the Swiss. I imagine the existence of powerful collective souls composed of all the inhabitants of a region, which shape the mind and values of the population, and make them weep, laugh, or grow angry together. Collective souls which expand or shrink or die, but which, as long as they are alive, control their inhabitants who are reduced to mere corpuscles. Here two hundred million corpuscles are pervaded by the vast American soul.

Sam is proud of these think tanks and cites figures, unaware that there is nothing more inexpressive than a number. One think tank has 593 specialists (or is it 1593), another costs 55 million dollars a year (or is it 155), and finally there is the secular monastery we are visiting, which hosts twenty people including psychologists (or is it psychiatrists), mathematicians (or physicists), sociologists (or chemists?). It's not really clear to me.

You say yes, yes to whatever they are telling you and pretend to be full of admiration and wonder, but only out of politeness, out of consideration for the person who is talking to you. I even go as far as to ask the question: "What do they study?"

"The enigmas of the man of the future."

Well, that's interesting. One of the six, the one with the slight stutter, says to me, "We are the only heretics."

"What do you mean by 'heretics'"?

"We do not approve."

In fact, he has the mocking eyes of a heretic, pale grey surrounded by a network of tiny wrinkles. But he does not have the expression of a heretic, he is not convinced, but rather dubious, and is more detached than pugnacious. Someone to get to know better.

Quite unexpectedly the one who bites his nails says very cordially, "Why don't you come and spend a few days with us? We have a guest room. Go and get your bags."

Sam winks at me from across the room. I believe I have understood why Sam, who barely knows me, has gone to all this trouble for me. He must have been a boy-scout as a child, required to do a good deed every day. He is a natural born missionary, the sort of man who insists on changing other people's minds, even if he has to cut off their heads to do so. This entronaut business bothers him and he is determined to make me forget about it.

I don't know how other people manage with their suitcases. For me they are always a problem, long before departure, when the moment comes to repack them. Someone packed them for me, perfectly. But if they are full, they begin to resemble certain children's toys: once everything inside has been removed there's no way to fit it all back in again. When empty they have the tendency to swell out, though nothing has been added, and I have never been able to figure out how and why this occurs. As soon as I arrive, I open the case and find everything in order. I try to maintain that order, taking things out very carefully: pyjamas, slippers, spongebag, etc. For the first couple of days everything goes fine. But then the morning rush, the evening tiredness, the departure for the next city, all contribute to create confusion. I can't find my socks, my handkerchiefs have vanished; I am in a terrible hurry, and this creates chaos. By now the battle is lost, and when I cut myself while shaving, I can't find the haemostatic. I go through my case frantically looking for my missing passport.

But there is an even greater problem: the transport of my bags. I can't handle the weight. I couldn't do so thirty years ago, as an army recruit in a damp fort in Gottardo. I stumbled under the weight of my sleeping bag, I lost my haversack, I dropped my gun. I was never cut out to be a soldier. Today with two suitcases, I am helpless. In Italy you can always find someone to carry your bags. In Germany, somewhat less, and in America never. In American hotels, the bellboys, all tall and strong, stand around chatting near the exit. They watch you pass by, burdened with your suitcases, umbrella, and bags, and follow you with an attentive eye. Perhaps they think you are trying to set a record. Or perhaps you have to call them, but I am shy and they are imposing. The taxi arrives (the driver is reading the comics), I hoist everything into the backseat with the last of my energy, trip on my umbrella, and fall onto the seat.

Here comes Sam with his tiny briefcase, his shirt intact, and a spotless handkerchief.

I didn't manage to visit the splendid garden of the lay monastery. They immediately began to interrogate me on the subject of entronautics. Surely Sam had told them about it. In order not to blabber on and on without their understanding, I beg them to listen to my opinion concerning thinkers and the mind. They agree, all quite curious. There are five left, the one with the disgusted face has gone away. We are sitting around a table on the veranda, and a maid is serving drinks. Sam is looking out at the sea, blue as the Aegean, but with the long waves of the ocean.

So I begin. The mind allows us to understand, right? We all need to understand, otherwise we feel uneasy. But does this need allow us to really understand ? The hungry mind demands food, i.e. an explanation. If it receives this food and is persuaded to eat it, and finds it edible, then hunger passes.

The Chinese peasant is convinced that during the winter the swallows burrow into the ground and become moles. That's fine with him, and he is content with this explanation. The British anthropologist is convinced that ten fossilized bones, arranged in a certain order, transform an anthropoid into man. That's fine with him and he is content with this explanation. They are both so content that they are irritated if someone contradicts them. Anyone who has eaten will refuse an emetic. When you are convinced of something, you don't want to begin doubting all over again. The mind is satisfied when it is persuaded, and believes this to be truth, in all good faith, which is unacceptable.

You thinkers, in this magnificent think tank, are wasting your time if you blindly trust the mind. The mind must always be checked and tested. Galileo – test it over and over again. If he checks it out, the Chinese peasant will realize that swallows do not become moles, and he will abandon his fantasy. And so will the English anthropologist, if, unable to go back in time a million years to check out his hypothesis, he takes it for what it really is – fantasies.

Truth is experiential. Sam, remember what we were saying about sugar? You are certain of it while you are tasting it. Cosmonautics is experiential – the moon cannot be touched with words. Entronautics is experiential: the inner universe can be reached only after many attempts.

I have finished, sages, now you may laugh at me.

I am a bit frightened. Like the Chinese peasant and the English anthropologist, I also have my cherished beliefs and convictions and it has taken me a lifetime to gather them and test them.

Though I state that I don't think much of science and scientists, at heart I share the obscure respect of my contemporaries, the respect that the ancients reserved for wise men and saints. I am afraid that these five men, paid to stay here and think in this beautiful villa on a California beach, will be able, with two short sentences, to strip me of my beliefs. So I am frightened. Will they laugh? Sam will certainly laugh at me; he thinks I am crazy.

But they do not laugh, rather they agree, and this gives me a feeling of relief. I like them more and more, we are united by the solidarity of seekers.

The stutterer with the grey eyes is a physicist. He must be about forty, and his authority is so great that you do not notice when he stutters, rather, you stutter if you answer him. He says, "Experience must guide the mind, and not the other way around. Take the electron as an example. We have a screen with two holes. The electron crosses from one side to the other, passing through both holes at the same time. Not that it splits in two, and one half goes through one hole and the other half through the other hole. No, it remains whole, and yet it passes through both holes simultaneously. For the mind that is impossible, yet in our experience, it is true. It is as though we could pass through two doors at the same time. But no, says the mind, that's impossible. Let it protest, let it starve if we have no explanation to feed it. Indeed, we haven't got one."

The thirty-year-old mathematician who bites his nails intervenes. "The mind is tricky because it is entrenched in habit. Take for example, symmetry. We have the habit of two eyes, two ears, mouth and nose in the middle, two arms, two legs, and the navel in the middle of the belly. For thousands of years we believed that symmetry was the law of the universe. It is not true. Biological life is left-handed, and nuclear life is asymmetrical. The nucleus of the atom is an inexhaustible producer of particles which appear for one billionth of a second. There are many kinds of particles, and new ones are being discovered every day, and if not discovered, then imagined. We have had to give up the idea of order in the midst of this anarchy. The mind cannot handle it. We have given a name to this mess. We call it 'the cloud of probability' and that is enough for us."

I ask, "Could this nuclear confusion be the projection of our inner chaos?"

They look at me with furrowed brows. I was unable to explain. I wanted to say that objectivity does not exist. It is a subject which is observing. But if the subject is in a state of chaos?

I do not insist. The conversation ends up on the subject of antimatter. It is suspected that in the midst of our sensible universe, another universe dwells, populated by other forces, other beings, with whom we co-exist, unawares. Perhaps the entronauts, in their descents and ascents, touch the continents of antimatter and explore them.

The next day we leave. I look at them in the garden for the last time. They wave goodbye from the veranda. I believe I have understood the reason for their stuttering, nervousness, and hesitation. Everything in them is uncertain, especially the future. Tomorrow the grey-eyed heretic may receive the Nobel prize or be kidnapped by the Chinese. Tomorrow the young man who bites his nails may discover the formula which will guarantee world peace or which will make the globe explode. Scientists are fragile. The discoveries of yesterday are shattered by those of today. They are chasing a dream in continual retreat.

Sunday, the day before I go back to New York, Sam proposes an afternoon at a nudist beach.

"Nudist?"

"Are you against nudity?"

Against it? No, frankly, I'm astonished. You never understand a man until you find out which God he prays to. Sam nudist? I thought you were a Christian. Against nudism? Why should I be? Rather I am not suited for it. Patched back together by surgeons after three operations . . . after all, you don't go to a gala celebration in a tattered suit. I am ashamed of my body. Sam nudist? I thought you were a Christian.

"A Christian, a Christian! Of course I am a Christian, but because of the Gospels, not to fatten a few hypocrites. You Catholics don't read the Holy Scriptures. You never carry a Bible in your suitcases. Jesus and the adulteress. He wouldn't let the others stone her, and he said to her, 'I do not condemn you.' We have all committed some form of adultery. Everyone of us, except Him. He was without sin, the only one who could throw the first stone, and he absolved her."

Sam in agitation, no longer the humorist I knew, but rather melancholy. I have just touched either his weak spot or his strength, but I am not sure which. Why nudist? As a protest, a liberation, or a purification? In any case, he is convinced.

"I've thought a lot about your entronauts. You didn't like the sages of Santa Barbara. You're planning a trip to Asia, and you think there's nothing to be found in America. But you're wrong. Here we are preparing a major revolution, a revolution which has never happened before: the revolution of Love. Come with me to the nudist beach, and you'll see what I'm talking about."

Oh no, Sam. What you are calling love is really sex. The sexual revolution, no thanks. I know all about those theories. No, you are confusing sex with love. This is the mistake of many philosophers who confuse man with his mind, the mistake of many politicians who confuse labour with pay. Don't dismember man, leave him whole. The sexual revolution. You might as well call it the buttock revolution. But what about all the rest? You simply amputate the rest of man's body.

Sam flares up, "I said love, not sex. You're always talking about entronauts, but you haven't yet realized that all lovers are entronauts."

He's right, it's true. Every lover is an entronaut, and perhaps every entronaut is a lover. All right Sam, don't get upset. I'll take off my clothes, despite my tattered body.

I have agreed to spend the afternoon with Sam at the nudist beach, but I feel very awkward and wish I hadn't come. I look around to see what you're supposed to do, so I can write about it later on. Boxing, monasteries, and now naked as a worm, a white worm, since I haven't been in the sun at all this year. With a tan, one is somehow less naked. Sam is hardly naked at all, behind his beard. I don't even have a moustache to hide me, even my face is naked.

Naked, white, patched, along the path leading to the sea, next to Sam, athletic, tanned, and bearded. We leave our clothes at the entrance. Here only couples are allowed in: a man and woman, a man and man, or two women. Never singles or families.

I try not to look around and to think quickly. The biblical story of Adam and Eve gave rise to the concept of Christian nudity, the universality of Greek art resides in the nudity of the statues, nakedness was the robe of the gods. Today, as all these people are stripping on the beach, art disdains the nude and renders it monstrous. The sad flesh of military recruits and public hospitals. But love redeems nudity. It requires nakedness and gives it back its beauty.

Though I am trying to think quickly, I have to watch where I put my feet. Accustomed to wearing shoes, my feet are defenceless. I worry about the sharp stones and the scorching sand, I knock my foot against the step and scrape my skin. As I am looking down at my feet, my eye encounters the other people. Good gracious: they are naked, naked and indifferent.

I tell myself that I don't have a paunch or a hunchback, and a few moments later I am indifferent too. A hunchback walks past very nonchalantly. Amid indifferent glances, magnificent young women plunge down from the diving board.

Sam leads me under an umbrella, where a group of his friends are gathered. He introduces me as hostile: European, Southern, Catholic, and hostile – they have me labelled. They view me as a bull in the ring. There are ten of them – men and women, young, beautiful, loquacious, all against me. When I don't understand or fall silent, Sam calmly translates for me.

Sam, why do you make me waste time, time and money? I'm looking for entronauts, not young men and women. First scientists, now nudists. Why?

He becomes serious, pauses, and then bursts out: "Because this entronaut business seems crazy to me. I hoped that at the monastery they would have changed your mind. They didn't, so I brought you here. Your entronauts are simply sexually inhibited people who are unconsciously seeking compensation. Don't get angry. Listen to me. Perhaps here in America we can spare you your disappointment in Asia."

I shrug my shoulders. Sam, you were not with me in India in 1965. You speak of entronauts the way an illiterate might speak of electronics. Anyway, you want to fight the bull, come on then and wave your flags.

The first to strike is a tall, stout man, as big as a Newfoundland dog. He would have been a perfect heavyweight, but instead he is an engineer. He has a young blonde attached to his arm, who watches him intently. He uses the socratic technique in his attack: first he asks questions, hoping to trick me with the answers. In order to deflate him, I only have to remain silent. Hold back the answers, and then slowly let them out when he has run out of air. He attacks.

"You were a child once, weren't you? You remember the repression? At home love could never be discussed, they either told you lies or shut you up with a slap. Right? Yet in the silence of the night when you suddenly woke up, you could hear your parents moaning. Remember the terrible shame of looking at a woman's breast? The blushes, the stupors, the search in the dictionary for words: genitals, etc. Do you remember, hypocrite? All this deforms us, and later in life we pay the price. We pay the price and we make others pay. How many men did Stalin massacre? And

Stalin went to seminary. Hitler was inhibited. So are your entronauts. . ."

Now be quiet, it's my turn. Do you have children? The blonde answers for him, for the moment we don't want any. Good enough, when you have a few, you can take them to bed with you and let them share the moaning. You haven't realized that sex education is useless, that love is irrational, and that love is sacred. You are two young carnivores, who suck the breasts of the mother, and when the milk has run out you sink in your teeth. At thirty you will be disillusioned, and forty, desperate, beneath the bites of your children. I have finished with you, mack, on with the next.

The next is a young girl with red hair, not the colour of carrots, but an intense red, like an Irish setter. Lovely hair and face. She is not aggressive, and so I calm down a bit.

I discover something that I would never have imagined possible. When everyone is stripped completely naked, you soon stop looking at the body. Your eyes seek out the faces, the body becomes an impersonal extra, nothing special. There is truly an adamic innocence in nakedness. Nudism is right. You won't believe it unless you try it. When they go into the snack bar on the beach, the women slip on a skirt and the men a pair of shorts. That little bit of cloth, that fig leaf, is enough to accentuate the bodies, to personalize them. The women become attractive, the men solid and virile. Outside, naked, you didn't notice. Eve did not cover herself out of shame, but out of coquettishness.

In a calm voice, the lovely red-head begins her attack.

No, I don't bite my mother. I understand her. She belongs to the last generation of girls who trembled at the risk of becoming mothers, whereas I belong to the first generation which need not tremble any more. After the bomb and the pill, the world has changed. Both have erased the boundaries, the boundaries between countries and between the sexes. Perhaps in ten years cosmonautics will be shown to be useless and will be abandoned. Entronautics? I don't know. Yet the progress of women is now irreversible. The freedom of women did not begin with the right to vote. It begins now. Woman is becoming what she always was, a female man. As a result everything will change. Couples will be equal, and the family will be different primarily because of one factor: only children who are wanted and loved will be born. Prostitution will vanish – prostitutes nearly always are young women with unplanned children they have to support. The shy maiden and the housewife will disappear, and so will the super-macho workaholic, the typical heart attack victim. We young people know this, that is why we dress the same. Women will become part of history, and everything will change. My mother cannot understand it, and neither can you.

Yet I do understand, everything will change, now that we are on the eve of the year 2000. People will hardly work at all, the class struggle will appear antediluvian, the famished populations will grow fat, and a little electronic machine will replace the whole bureaucratic apparatus of governments. Women will openly choose their men, as men have chosen women. There will be no more harems in the Islamic countries and wife-swapping will cease. Divorces will follow and precede marriages. But we will continue to die.

We will continue to live very brief lives and to be dead for a long, long time. Do you understand? There will come a day when everyone will be dead, except me. And so what's the point? So what good is it to make history, to work, to take initiative in the business of love. What good is it to decorate a place where we will remain but an instant?

I caress the red hair of the Irish setter. I speak to her in Italian, and she doesn't understand:

You see, little girl, Sam believes I am crazy, I am a mad man who doesn't want to die. Not because I am attached to this ragged flesh, but because I want to have an aim to my existence. I want to play all the cards, even the most improbable ones. Someone has claimed that instead of dying we pass to the other side, intact. You may choose to be an insignificant soul carrying a cadaver, or a soul bearing immortality. All the entronauts say so. In 1965, near one of them, death seemed to me an impossibility, and therefore I must search for them. Perhaps your mother might understand. You cannot.

Sam, I'm leaving. You have gone to a lot of trouble for me and I thank you. I would like to have had the opportunity to get to know you better. The only things I know about you are your beard, your interest in nudism and in the Gospel. But my time is up and I have to leave. I have hardly any dollars left. There are no entronauts in America, and I have crossed the Atlantic in vain.

There are entronauts in America, as I discovered unexpectedly in New York, when I telephoned Essy Mills to say hello. Tomorrow I'm flying back to Europe. She said to me, "Come and visit me."

I went to her house in New Jersey, an hour by

subway from Manhattan. She has a tiny, meagre garden, inhabited by a neutered cat who, when he isn't seeking attention, lies curled up asleep.

Essy, tall and slender, is not the same person I saw in Madison Square Garden. Without her wig she has short hair and a long neck. She seems even younger, about twenty. Without her make-up her eyes become tender, like a young deer's. I find again the large mouth, the cute nose, the bronze skin, the enchanted expression, the gentle manner, and the ringing voice.

A few pieces of furniture in the room, nothing special. This is the poverty of young journalists all over the world, they pay you little and when they have squeezed you dry, they throw you away. I have known quite a few young journalists, always convinced that they will soon write a book. Inside every journalist is the melancholy of a book never born.

She offers me whisky, but I prefer tea. It's clear that she wants to speak to me about something, but doesn't dare. She asks, "Did your trip to California go all right?"

I do not answer. I try to be open and friendly towards her, letting her draw in closer to me.

She says, "You must be content with your life. *Une vie réussie est un rêve d'adolescent, realisé dans l'âge mûr.*"

She likes French quotations. Why should I tell her how dissatisfied I am with myself? I maintain my affectionate silence.

"Did you know my grandfather was an Amerind?"

In these parts they use the expression Amerind instead of "Indian" or "redskin".

I had suspected something of the kind. I encourage her to confide in me. "Tell me about your grandfather."

"Yes, he was an Amerind. He married a French woman. Who knows how that happened. He was very handsome as a young man, and even in his old age. He died six months ago. They had a daughter, my mother, she was taken to France. She fell in love with an American and came back to America. Just think, two people make love and you are born, the grandchild of an Amerind of the Southwest."

"Does it disturb you?"

"No, he was an important man. Of all my family, he was the only one of any importance. Are you a Catholic?"

She is trying to change the subject, so I help her. "And are you a Protestant?"

"My father was a Methodist minister. I had to learn the Bible by heart. You can't imagine how frightened I was, and how much I cried as a child over the shouts, curses, wrath, and bloody revenge of Jehovah against the Jews, who were his chosen people. It's a good thing you Catholics don't read the Bible. I detest preachers who pretend to know God's thoughts, wishes, and plans, as if they were his bosom buddies, and knew his moods. Do you remember Broadway? I asked you if you weren't tired of that old word. Do you know what peyote is? Do you know who Tsa Toke is?"

Tsa Toke, the Kiowa painter and Black Elk, the Sioux ascetic. Two names impressed in my memory. Now I understand. Essy has an Indian grandfather, Tsa Toke had a white grandmother; Tsa Toke, a great painter, the greatest Amerind painter, now famous today. His brief life was spent in the shadows.

He was born in 1904, near Fort Sill, Oklahoma, of the Kiowa race – a sturdy handsome people, wandering hunters of the prairie who migrated from the source of the Missouri River to the Arkansas River, following their prey. Tsa Toke means hunter of horses.

The white grandmother had been taken captive as a child in 1870, during an attack against the invader. The Kiowa killed more settlers than all the others, more than the Apaches or the Comanches. But they spared a young blonde girl who became the bride of a Kiowa warrior and the mother of Kiowa children.

Tsa Toke was born on the reservation, that is a form of forced house arrest. Ex-nomads in a cage, ex-dominators in chains, a whole people once numerous reduced to a thousand survivors, robbed of everything: land, food, language, religion, tradition. In exchange, they were given the Bible and alcohol.

He was born with the Kiowa gift for painting. This tribe was famous for the ideograms with which they recorded their history until 1892. After that they stopped painting. Then Tsa Toke was born, and from his early childhood his hands were always painting. As a young boy he was given a place around the tribal fire, where the elders held counsel, repeated ancient myths, and celebrated the cult of peyote, more ancient than the Aztecs. Peyote was the only part of their heritage left. In it they found themselves again; they found an inner power, a path to follow, a reason to survive.

Tsa Toke reveals to us a bit of the Amerind mystery. The mystery of faces which seem inexpressive, behind which lies a sensitive soul, which closes up when it is misunderstood, and becomes proud and stoic. A soul which in nature sensed the existence of the great divine spirit and attempts to reach it through the cult of peyote.

Great painters seize reality before others notice it. It is only after Velasquez that Madrid now has the skies that everyone admires today. Only after Monet has London had the fog that we see today, only after Tsa Toke has peyote and its cult become intelligible to us.

Tsa Toke very rarely left the reservation. The first time was at age fourteen: he claimed that he wanted to paint things that the white man could not imagine. They sent him back to the reservation. Then in 1930, his paintings were exhibited in Gallup. A few people saw them, and they began to talk about him in San Francisco. Susannah Peters spoke a lot about him, but with little result. No one was interested in the paintings of the redskins. Yet he was already preparing his series on peyote and writing a commentary to them.

One day in 1936, Susannah Peters, returning home, found a package containing paintings and a manuscript outside her door. There was a note from Tsa Toke's wife, "He said to give you these things." He was dead.

Peyote is a cactus. Its botanical name is *Lophophore*. Sacred substances to eat or breathe in: the soma of the Vedas, the hemp of the Zoroastrians, the wine of Dionysius, the tea of Zen, the Mexican mushroom, the peyote of the Amerinds, the incense of the Christians, and so on.

Essy gets up, goes to the cupboard, and takes out an antique bowl full of small seeds.

Peyote seeds.

She places the cup between us. We are silent. I ask her, "What is it that is bothering you?"

"I wanted to ask you . . . My grandfather taught me the ritual. When I went to visit him in his village, it was all very natural. Now he is dead. I don't know if I should continue, or if it's a good thing to continue. I am very much alone. You talked to me about entronauts and so I thought . . . you might be able to give me some advice . . . "

She bursts out weeping. I take her hand and this

gesture of affection makes her sob. She continues, "I feel so lost now that he is gone. Shipwrecked."

She recovers, dries her eyes, blows her nose, excuses herself, and pours me some more tea. She concludes, "Please don't think I'm a drug addict."

"No, of course not. Drug addicts are victims of chemistry. One drop of LSD is five thousand times stronger than the Mexican plant from which it is derived. Chemistry is diabolical. It takes a sacred substance and converts it into a drug. It could even transform incense in the church and drive all the people at mass insane. How many times have you done the ritual?"

"Three times, once a year: the last time was last year."

"Tell me about the first time."

"How can I tell you about it? The journey, the days of purification, the explanation, the night, the tranquillity, the fire, the ritual. Then the mystery and the encounter. I don't know how to describe it. The words "mystic", "cosmic", "transcendent", won't do. Have you ever read Tsa Toke?"

"Call it sacred, a sacred encounter."

"Yes, sacred. An incredible sense of peace. Thoughts vanish, the last ones leave very, very slowly, like distant birds flying through the sky. An unimaginable silence. Then happiness. You feel boundless love, and that you yourself are loved endlessly. There are no words. Not even Tsa Toke . . . "

"And afterwards?"

"Afterwards, a new life, with new meanings."

She is silent, suddenly embarrassed. She tries to change the subject. "You are Catholic, so perhaps you don't understand. Don't the hypocrites of the Gospel bother you?"

"There are a lot of hypocrites and a lot of pharisees, but also a lot of saints."

This young girl looks at me with the frightened eyes of a doe. "He died six months ago. What should I do?"

I would like to say to her, Essy, lovely American entronaut, you have had the encounter, now you must make your life sacred. The aim is to make our hidden side emerge.

EUROPEAN JOURNEY

Once back in Rome after my trip to New York I prepared my article on boxing. To my great surprise I discovered that Edoardo had left the magazine. He was now working for television, and they had sent him to the Congo on assignment. The world is like an airport, everyone is always going somewhere. Turn away briefly, and a second later the man standing next to you is gone.

My book? My journeys? My search for the entronauts began to vanish enveloped by the thick fog of daily routine. But I kept my intention alive by reading books and writing letters here and there, to people whose existence was doubtful, and whose addresses I was unsure of. Most of these letters came back stamped by the post office: *No longer at this address, addressee unknown, deceased.*

Then one day I got an answer.

At that time I was doing a good deal of reading on that age-old question – the body and the soul. Some people believe only in the body. Once dead, we leave behind our corpse as a frightening survivor. Some people believe only in the soul. Once it leaves the body, it is either sent to heaven or to hell.

I do not agree with the first group. Thoughts are not corporeal. My own thoughts are at times wrinkled and gnarled, at other times they are limpid, inexpressible, but they most certainly do not stem from the brain. They come from somewhere higher. Nor are my emotions visceral. The enchantment which overwhelms me while contemplating the work of Beato Angelico, the boundless sense of wonder while looking out at the sea in Capri, the bitterness I feel when faced with human evil, and with my own wickedness. There is no organ in the human body which causes feelings of hope to arise in the heart when touched. So I cannot agree with the first group.

Nor can I agree with the latter. A corpse of course has no thoughts and feelings, but where have they gone, where have our intelligence and our goodness gone? To the gods or to God? Which god or gods? The judge? The creator of billions of men destined from the beginning to suffer hell everlasting? We pardon criminals serving life terms after thirty years in prison. Is God less forgiving than we are? It would be blasphemy to assert such a thought, therefore I cannot agree with the latter.

At that time I was reading piles of books and writing endless letters. I was searching for the truth regarding the body and the soul, for a truth that someone had directly experienced. But I wasn't getting anywhere.

Then one day I got an answer.

Someone had told me that in Paris there existed a group of people working on out-of-the-body experiences. That's all I knew. Out-of-the-body. What does that mean? Perhaps spiritism (exhumation of psychic corpses), theosophy (spiritual mish-mash) or perhaps parapsychology (which measures the soul's infinity with a tailor's tape measure) or perhaps occultism (an ambiguous word, including everything, even charlatans).

Amid these uncertainties, two books arrived from Paris, quite old, dated 1926. The author used the pseudonym "Yram". The book was published by Adyar, and printed by *"L'emancipatrice"*. The address was given: rue de Pondicherry.

What a coincidence. It was in Pondicherry that I had met a great French writer, who concealed his identity under the name of Satprem. At the time of our encounter, he was very ill. I will never forget the expression in his eyes, a deep, heart-rending tenderness. We were sitting on a terrace, under a shining white sky, discussing the body and the soul.

"Our consciousness may free itself from the body and leave it behind, but you must be careful where you exit from. If you leave through the heart, it's all right. If you leave through the head, it can be dangerous."

"Is it really possible?"

Satprem, already thinking about something else, as if this were a fact everybody knew, continued in the low, soft voice of the sick. "These experiences are as old as the world, as old as man."

In his book, printed in rue de Pondicherry, Yram recounts that for twelve years, from 1914 – 1926, he journeyed outside his body. He described these experiences in detail and said that he would give more details in person.

Denise, my friend in Paris who had sent me these books, included a note, "The author died in 1935. I'll try to find out more." Yram offered what I was looking for, direct experience of truth. But I could no longer meet him personally.

The people we would like to have met are nearly always dead: Aurobindo, Angela of Foligno, Oppenheimer, the Russian pilgrim, the Portugese nun, and others. I added Yram to this list.

I wrote another letter to the Paris publisher requesting information on Yram. After so many *"No forwarding address. Addressee unknown. Deceased"* I hardly hoped to receive an answer.

Instead a letter arrived from the publisher, including the address where Yram had lived forty years ago. An address. A clue. But I had to go to Paris and for the moment that was out of the question. I didn't have the money for the trip.

Money is a problem which requires a clarification. It is an extremely obscure matter.

The first, most obvious and annoying enigma of money is that there are many people who seem to have loads of it to throw away and you never understand where they get it from. That guy who always says hello to you, that you seem to run into everywhere, who has a big car, beautiful women, a house in the very best neighbourhood, a yacht, the one who is always sending you postcards from exotic places, the one who once confessed to you that he was an orphan, the one whom you once asked, curious, "But what do you do for a living?".

Who answered frankly, cordially, and yet mysteriously, "I do a bit of everything, whatever comes my way."

I wonder what it is that comes his way. Money never comes my way. I have to grab it somewhere.

The second enigma is that wealthy people are often simple people and frequently ignorant and silly people who would seem incapable of setting up a small shop on their own, but who in reality run a hundred supermarkets. You look at these mysterious beings and feel like an idiot.

The third enigma is that intelligent men and women, capable, industrious, hard-working, can barely eke out a living, often burden themselves with debts, and die worn out and destitute. This occurs at every level of society, among career people, factory workers, intellectuals, artists, and peasants. The best and most practical skills often do not bring money.

Perhaps money has certain preferences. Perhaps it is attracted to the silly and repelled by the intelligent.

As for me, I can only travel if a magazine sends me on assignment. Though I deeply wanted to go to Paris on the trail of Yram, I did nothing to get myself sent there.

I hadn't sought such an assignment, and I had no money. Instead, I ended up in London.

And so one evening, somewhat unexpectedly, I found myself in London. In the morning I was in Rome, and the idea of a trip was the furthest thing from my mind. I had gone to the foreign press bureau to see if there were any letters for me. I found John there – French radio newscaster, son of an American mother and an Italian father, who married a Swiss girl. He's never without his tape recorder. He speaks all languages and could interview the deaf and dumb. He is one of the best in his profession, and yet he is always broke. But who understands how money works anyway?

Our friendship is exhilarating. Just seeing each other puts us both in a good mood. He pretends to hate writers. I pretend to hate journalists. He asks me if I have finally stopped writing, I ask him if he has finally learned how to. After all, he doesn't need to: with radio, TV, and tape recorders, journalists don't need to know how to read and write. "Well," he replies, "you writers are illegible and so nobody reads you."

When this banter has finished, we speak about

serious things. He has an idea: "Why don't you go to London? I have to give up my seat on a special tour to inaugurate a new chain of English hotels. Why don't you take my place?"

"London, no thanks. Paris, yes. What would I do in London in this season, with the fog?"

"What would you do? Take a ten-day holiday. In the very best hotels, all paid for. Besides, the plane might make a stop-over in Paris. Please take my place. I'd be really sorry to leave it empty. I promised I'd go. When you come back, jot down a couple of pages and I'll tape them. Come on, please help me."

Anyway, after all that, I found myself that afternoon on a plane with thirty journalists, sitting next to the leader of the expedition, whom I happened to know by sight. Knowing someone by sight doesn't mean that you know him. We've been running into each other for nearly ten years, and every time we meet, we greet each other with a faint smile, though we know absolutely nothing about each other. I don't even know his name, nor does he know mine.

I ask him, "Are we stopping over in Paris?"

"No, we're proceeding directly to London."

Aware of his duties as leader of the expedition, he tries to strike up a conversation. "Still interested in those problems, are you? Very interesting."

Who knows what that means? Then he adds, with a polite little lie, "Yes, your latest book was very interesting indeed."

He finds a better subject of conversation. "When you are in London, you must meet Mrs. Maggie McCann. Do you know her? An extraordinary woman. Simply extraordinary. Let me give you a note of introduction. She is omnipotence."

Whatever is that supposed to mean? He must have

mistaken me for someone else. He scribbles a few lines on the back of his calling card and then hands it to me, repeating the words, "She's omnipotence".

He gets up and walks down the aisle, going from one journalist to the next, performing his duties as leader of the expedition. I look at the note and am astonished. He has written my name correctly. What on earth is this omnipotence business?

We are in the skies over France, heading towards the Channel. We are not landing in Paris. I will be unable to track down Yram. I close my eyes.

I think about how difficult it is to open up to others. We are lazy. We only know the surface of the people around us. We are mute oysters. Who is John, who has given me this opportunity to go to London? I don't know. I only know that we see each other now and again, put each other in a good mood, and exchange a few joking insults. We are too lazy to go beyond the surface.

I remember Aldo, an American colleague who worked with me during the war. We were friends – Hey Aldo, how's it going? Just great, and you? Later on, whenever we met, I always found him a little heavier and he always found me a bit thinner.

One summer afternoon I met him in the reading room of the foreign news bureau. He was hiding his nose in a handkerchief.

"What happened to you?"

"No, it's nothing. I fell, that's all. A nosebleed."

"Do you need anything? Shall I drive you home?"

He declined and went home alone. I can still see him. He went home, turned on the gas, and killed himself. He was so desperate that he wanted to die, but he said nothing. There was nothing I could have done to help him, though we worked together and were friends. Mute oysters.

One summer day, Aldo went home alone in silence and detached his soul from his body.

Maggie McCann is an extraordinary woman, mistress of omnipotence. I misjudged the leader of the expedition. One easily misjudges if one looks only at the surface of things.

I went to visit Maggie one boring Sunday morning when I didn't know what else to do. The boredom of British Sundays is dense and oppressing. In 1830, Thomas de Quincey claimed that it was this boredom which had driven him to opium, and a hundred years later Robert Byron warned travellers that few visitors manage to survive a Sunday in Glasgow without going mad.

I leave the hotel, hail a cab, and show the driver the note with Maggie's address which the leader of the expedition had given me. The man looks at the address, reads the note, re-reads it, then announces that he does not know that street and goes away. London is so big that no taxi driver knows his way around all of it. I go out into the fog, plunge down into the Tube and have better luck.

Maggie lives in the suburbs, in one of those London streets which stretch on endlessly for kilometres and kilometres, with rows and rows of little one-storey houses with a tiny garden, all alike, painted the same colour, with identical doors and windows, all interchangeable. Perhaps even the people who live in them are interchangeable.

I find the number, go through the gate, and check the name on the plaque. I press the button and can hear the bell ringing inside.

There's no going back now. I straighten my tie and

check my buttons. Brisk footsteps inside approach, the door swings open wide, and a man in a smoking jacket with a colonel-like air about him appears. Indeed, he is the typical English colonel: tall, thin, with a moustache, big nose and grey eyes, sparse blond hair parted on the side.

"McCann?"

"Yes?"

I hand him the note. He reads it and then explodes into hospitality. He speaks a smattering of Italian. Come in, come in. During the war he spent a couple of years in Rome. Good gracious, of course, come in.

"You have come for omnipotence. A writer. Yes, yes, of course."

He is Maggie's husband. Not a colonel, an ex-captain, ex-functionary, now in retirement.

"Maggie will be down in a moment. She's writing in her room. Answering letters from all over the world. Too many, too many."

He has me sit in an armchair in the living room, next to a fireplace where a coal fire is burning. I feel rather awkward. I know nothing about these people. Who are they? What is omnipotence? How will I explain my visit?

I look around. A few pieces of antique English furniture, a rare *blanc de Chine*, a Robertson watercolour depicting the head of a bulldog.

"Bulldog?"

"You too?"

I am saved. We are both bulldog lovers. I take out the photo of my dog and show it to the captain. Then he goes out and comes back with a white bulldog, very handsome and muscular, who noisily sniffs my trousers and wags his tail. The common love for bulldogs is better than any blood relationship.

I hear a light step descending the staircase. It is Maggie. The dog runs towards her as she appears smiling in the doorway. She is a small blonde woman, only her neck reveals her real age – forty – she has a lovely face with delicate features and laughing almond-shaped eyes, the kind of eyes that charmed Baudelaire.

She looks at me, greets me, and invites me to tea.

Ten days in London, ten days with Maggie. I am attracted by the secret of omnipotence. Maggie is also an entronaut. Not like Essy Mills, of Indian blood. Essy, who has had a sacred encounter and must now render her life sacred, a tremendous undertaking. Not like Yram and Satprem, who leave their bodies riding on their souls, a tremendous adventure. Maggie has discovered that the control room of our destiny is inside ourselves. The mechanisms of omnipotence are within us. A simple truth, but difficult to understand and even more difficult to put into practice.

Maggie has never written any books, nor does she intend to write any. She flees from fame and publicity. Every afternoon she receives three or four people and helps them live. Every morning she replies to the letters of the people who write to her. She will accept nothing, and is not interested in money, though she teaches others how to become rich.

Now and then, when she is overwhelmed by too many people, her husband takes her away to another part of London, giving no one their address except for a few close friends, among whom is the leader of the expedition. Who would have ever thought? Closed oysters.

In Maggie's company, the oysters open up. Perhaps because of her serenity. Smiling and petite, she radiates serenity. The captain is serene, the dog is serene.

One day a man about forty comes, crippled by problems: money, family, love. He is suffocating and no longer has the energy to save himself; he can only weep.

Maggie listens to his story all the way to the end and then asks in her soft, gentle voice, "What is your wife like?"

"Sullen, stubborn and hostile."

"And your lover?"

"She used to be very sweet. Now she is sullen, stubborn, and hostile."

"And your business partner?"

"He used to be a close friend, but now he is sullen, stubborn, and hostile."

"Why?"

"Because our business is about to go bankrupt."

"No, if you were to take another wife, lover, or business partner, the same thing would happen, they would all become sullen, stubborn, and hostile."

"An unchangeable destiny?"

"It can change, if you change."

"But how can I change?"

This is Maggie's secret, the secret to discover: how to change your destiny.

Another day a young girl came – newly married and deeply in love with her husband. Her problem was that she was very jealous, afraid of the other woman.

"What other woman?"

"I don't know who. The other woman."

"Dear, don't you see you have made it all up?"

I begin to understand. It seems to us that our miseries come from outside, but rather they come from inside us. We form them with our very substance. "My business is going bankrupt," "I'm afraid of the other woman." We attract what we fear. Man doesn't receive what he deserves, but rather what he resembles.

How to change one's destiny? Through certainty.

I finally understood one morning while visiting Maggie. The captain had taken the dog out for a walk. There was no fog that day. First you could feel a faint hint of the sun, and then it became fully visible. London was beautiful.

I got on a bus at Piccadilly Circus. If a foreign visitor walks around Piccadilly Circus for about fifteen minutes, he is sure to run into some friend of his, just arrived in London, but I did not wait fifteen minutes. I got on the bus after waiting briefly in a queue. In London you spend a lot of time waiting in queues. If three people should happen to form a queue quite by accident on the street, the passers-by will stop and queue up behind them automatically.

Today London is full of light, seen from atop of a double decker. The wide pavements of Regent Street are crowded with people out enjoying the precious morning sun – the typists in miniskirts (but they have a military gait), young policemen conducting traffic with calm gestures, posters advertising nearly every pianist in the world and the birth of tiger cubs at the zoo, antique shop signs, charwomen scrubbing doorways – with cigarettes dangling from the corner of their mouths, wandering dogs, the window at the chemist's displaying remedies for the two national ailments: the common cold and constipation.

I get off and walk down the street where Maggie lives. It's rather unkind to criticize these identical little houses with their tidy lawns and their front doors painted white. If you live in the fog, you must withdraw into yourself. In Naples you can live and die out of doors. But not here. The sun is precious and rare. Here everyone must have his own house and open the white door with his own key without having to ring the doorbell: inside a man's refuge and his kingdom.

How can we change our destiny? Through certainty.

Now that the captain has gone out with the dog, Maggie is busy tidying up the house, wearing rubber gloves and a scarf on her head. She greets me warmly. Her almond eyes are smiling. She is surprised by the flowers I have brought her, and offers me tea, but I decline. I curl up in an armchair and watch her. Her presence is very reassuring. John, that gossip who sent me here to England, would say that I am falling in love with her. But I've always been in love with her. I seek serenity and she is serenity itself.

The doorbell rings and I go to answer. It is the desperate man who came the other day. He needs Maggie. Maggie is already there, removing her gloves and scarf, leading him into the sitting room, getting him to talk.

"I'm finished."

Though he is an Englishman he weeps unashamed, despite my presence. Then he blows his nose, sobs, and puts his hand on his mouth like a child. One could never ridicule him or accuse him of weakness. He is overcome with desperation. The poor man says, "I have been abandoned by everyone. There is no one left."

"You still have yourself."

"How can I save myself if I am alone?"

"Through certainty. Not hope, not faith, but certainty."

Change one's destiny, discover abundance. We all want abundance, we all feel we deserve it. Why is it that we lack it? Why is it that we lack health, love, and good luck? What we lack is certainty. Rather we are afraid.

To an elderly banker, Maggie says (she calls everyone by their first name. It's the English equivalent to informal address), "You look frightened, Paul."

"It's true. I am full of fears. Mainly cancer. I think about it constantly. And then car accidents. That I'll die in a crash and suffocate to death or burn to death. Then war. I have seen so many. And then money. The pound is plummeting down. Haven't you read the papers?"

"Don't read them, Paul. They only terrify you. Be careful not to read them, not to watch television, not to listen to the radio. You live in terror, Paul. How can you keep on living with all these fears?"

Free us from fear and all its children: shyness, rancour, jealousy, anger, hatred, revenge. It is discontent, the eldest daughter, who is growing ever-stronger, making us more and more desolate. She drags us down and we grow accustomed to this out of inertia: it is easier to wallow in bitterness than to ascend to joy. And there is also a certain form of pleasure in feeling that we are the victims of the universe.

To a woman who has been abandoned by her husband, Maggie says, "There's a strange pleasure in it. Fear is a drug. You can't do without it. But the universe does not hate you, it loves you. That's the truth, Ruth. It loves you."

"It loves me. That's news. But I am nothing, I am no one."

"Ruth, the whole universe would be different if even one of us had never been born. We have all changed the universe and we continue to change it. We are necessary, rather we are indispensable. Ruth, do you want your husband to come back to you?"

"That's all I want and hope for."

"Don't hope, don't have faith. Be certain. Go home,

Ruth, get his bed ready, as though he were coming home tonight. Set a place for him at the table as though he had called to say he was coming. Don't talk about him, don't hate the other woman, don't judge him, don't condemn him. Make yourself attractive, because he is about to come back to you. You have to purge yourself of all the fear you have accumulated over the years. When you are full of certainty, then he will return."

When two different individuals, with different psychic constitutions, are faced with the same events, one will find fortune, the other disaster. The latter, out of fear, will let opportunity slip, aggravating his situation and catapulting himself into misfortune, whereas the other will have got rich in the meantime. We have within us the controls of our destiny, and we can manipulate them as we wish.

I ask her, "And if I should be defeated?"

"Call it victory and it will be so."

Like many English people, Blake the poet-painter and Wallace the scientist, Maggie often speaks about angels. To a student who is uncertain whether to leave university or try a different one, Maggie says, "Have you asked your angel?"

"What angel?"

"The one you have inside you. Didn't you know that it was there?"

"No, where?"

"Behind your back, just a bit above the head."

"An angel?"

"Yes. Others call it saint or virgin. It's a presence. Ask it to guide you and it will help you."

For some this is incredible. But many ridiculed the aeroplane until two brothers who mended bicycles for a living flew through the air, sustained by certainty. The universe abounds in wealth and goodness for all its creatures. In order to be filled, we must open ourselves and not close up. There is a technique for doing this, as in all experimental science. There are rules and for each rule a treatise could be written.

First rule: Free oneself from fear. Watch over your thoughts, especially those subterranean thoughts which are barely visible, and which are the vestiges of childhood fears, conditioning, and ancestry. Uproot the thought which oppresses you.

Second rule: Fill yourself with certainty. The certainty of every good thing. If your old inner deformation reduces you to doubt, then build images of abundance for yourself. Doors opening for you, roads lined with flowers, open chests filled with gold. Invent phrases, rhythms, rhymes, and repeat them constantly, as often as you have swallowed anxious thoughts. Repeat them until you are full of certainty.

Third rule: Before abundance reaches you, give thanks. Thank your angel, saint, virgin, luck, the universe, the presence, the name is unimportant. It is important to give thanks as though we have already received abundance when there is still not the slightest sign that it is on the way. This is indispensable for it gives wings to abundance. Not only give thanks, but behave as though you have already received it. If you are about to receive money, spend it because it has already arrived. If you are about to receive health, get out of bed because you have already been healed. If you are about to receive love, sing because you are already loved.

Fourth rule: Give your blessing. It is not easy, as arid as we are, but it is health-giving to bless. Find a benediction in your heart and let it expand. Bless those who love you and those who do not. Bless those whom you meet and those who are far away. Bless when you give and when you receive. Bless the past and the future. Bless your life because it presents no obstacles, enemies, rivalries. Life puts each one of us to the test. You are the companion of certainty and abundance. Always give your blessing.

This is Maggie's form of entronautics. Of course, the experts laugh at her. They are right, because they have already sought and found their abundance: in incredulity, in negativeness and bitterness, and that's all they will receive.

So the question of money has been cleared up. It used to seem so obscure.

I used to think, so many people seem to have money to throw away, and I have no idea where they get it from. Now I understand. In order to receive money continuously, it is necessary to give it freely. What you give to others, you give to yourself. If you do not obey the impulse to give, then you close yourself. If you slow down the outflow, then you also slow down the inflow of abundance. It is a law of hydraulics.

Now I understand that guy in Rome who is always saying hello to me.

"What do I do for a living? Whatever comes my way."

Things come his way, but not mine. It's only natural. He keeps himself open and waits, but I wait for nothing, I retreat into my writing. I don't even fantasize. We possess what we have in our mind. If we can't imagine something, we certainly cannot possess it.

Now I understand why so many wealthy people are simple, ignorant, even silly. Why should a wealthy man be intelligent? He need only be convinced deep down in his soul, of this secret. He builds his fortune on his deep certainty.

Now I understand why so many capable, industrious and hard-working men and women die worn out and destitute after so much toil. Everyone lives his life as he imagines it. Nothing is easier to imagine than fear. It is the opposite of omnipotence.

Omnipotence is no secret. It's a method.

I find Maggie alone. It is my last morning. Tomorrow I am leaving. She is wearing her rubber gloves and head scarf, and is busily dusting. She greets me warmly. Her almond eyes are full of enchantment, and as usual, she is surprised by the flowers I have brought her. I curl up in an armchair and watch her while she works.

How did this unknowing entronaut, this tiny, blonde, simple English woman with the soft voice, discover the method of omnipotence? Did she discover it while caring for her house, her captain, and her bulldog?

I ask her and she answers without hesitation.

"In the Gospel. You Catholics . . . "

"Maggie, don't you start in. I know the New Testament very well and have read it many times."

"Then you will remember . . . " She begins to quote very seriously: "If ye have faith as a grain of mustard seed, ye might say unto this sycamine tree, Be thou plucked up by the root and be thou planted in the sea; and it should obey you." "These are the words of Jesus Christ, quoted by St. Luke. 'Ask and you shall receive.' If you have faith the size of a mustard seed, then nothing is impossible."

In a soft lyrical voice, she sings me a few lines of a hymn. "Consider the lilies of the field, how they grow; they toil not, neither do they spin. Take therefore no thought for the morrow, for the morrow shall take care of itself."

Then she runs to a drawer and takes out a Bible. She offers it to me as a memento.

I cannot accept this gift. "No, I have an Italian one. You have already given me an archangel."

"Isn't it an angel?"

"No, it is an archangel, and I have already begun to talk to it."

The captain and his bulldog return. A nice man, he ought to have been a colonel. Lovely dog, as nice as mine. Bye Maggie. She stands on her tiptoes to kiss me on the cheek. Dear, dear Maggie. The three of them escort me to the gate. I say goodbye again before plunging down into the Tube.

Why must I always be leaving? Wherever I am, I always feel the urge to put down roots: in 1965 in Pondicherry, in 1966 in New York. But there's always a wind blowing me somewhere else. I would have liked to settle down in London near Maggie. Her little house in the suburbs seems to me a perfect home, where I could live in the company of real friendship, where I surely would have found serenity.

Where will this wind blow me now? Tonight I will return to Rome, though I would like very much to go to Paris. I feel sad, although I shouldn't. Omnipotence is a state of mind.

It is evening and a heavy fog envelops Waterloo Bridge where I stand looking down at the Thames. The streetlamps shine a soft flannel grey in the dark blanket of fog. Down on the river barges appear, like black insects and then are swallowed up. The fog is so thick that I feel completely alone, so I address my Archangel and say, "So then I am not going to Rome, I am going to Paris."

Voices in me cry, "Impossible, impossible", but I refuse to listen. Back in the hotel again, the leader of the expedition greets me with a smile. He has telephoned Maggie who has informed him of our friendship. He apologizes to me, "The return will be a bit long, I'm afraid. Five French journalists are joining us and so we're stopping over in Paris."

Astonished, I forget to thank my Archangel.

Paris in the morning, on the traces of Yram, the navigator of the soul. I have left the letter with the publisher's address at home in Rome. As soon as I collect my bags, I'll telephone the publisher.

Paris in May, blue skies. In London when a bit of blue appears in the sky, people lean out of the windows of the buses to admire it and point it out to each other. People celebrate sunshine the way Alexandria of Egypt celebrated rain.

I have a hard time locating my bags at Orly. I finally discover them, abandoned and alone with no porters in sight. I grab them and make my way towards the distant telephone booth.

Paris in May, a lovely sun. When I ring the publishing house, I find the secretary in a negative mood. An address? Whose address? Yram? He is not one of our authors. Forty years ago! Out of print. The director? He's out of town. He'll be back next month.

Paris is beautiful in May, but to my eyes it is losing its splendour. I will ring Denise, my friend who sent me the two books by Yram and who promised to find out more information. An editor for a publishing house, she lives amid books. The honeyed voice of her secretary answers. She too today is on the side of the NO's. "Denise isn't here. In Bordeaux. I don't know when she'll be back. No, she didn't leave anything. What is

your name? No, nothing. You want to come by anyway.
Come then."

I decide to go to her office anyway because she
might have written to me in Rome, and I may find the
copy of her letter on file. Instead I find her secretary,
beautiful and stupid. The beauty of young girls is often
only one side of the coin, the other side is stupidity,
and they are often as dull-witted as they are beautiful.
The more I look at her, the more I realize how lovely
she is. Her make-up, hair-style, and dress are all
modern, but her beauty is timeless. My grandfather
would have found her attractive and so would my son.
Denise, how do you manage to keep this delightful
goose?

She knows nothing, has no information; she doesn't
remember. She is acting a bit as she bats her eyes at
me. She knows my name and my address because
Denise dictates my letters to her. Rome is beautiful,
n'est-ce pas? She'd like to visit there sometime. She
offers me no help, and yet I find her touching. I know
what a heavy burden feminine beauty can be.

She is convinced that I intend to translate a book
and I am unable to dissuade her. She meditates, "Body
and soul. Isn't that the title of a famous novel?" Then
suddenly brightening, "Yes, we are reading a
manuscript on that subject at the moment. *Bicorporal*,
or something like that. Wait a moment."

She takes a manuscript out of a drawer and hands it
to me. I glance at it rather diffidently; Author: Arthur
Leroy. Title: *Disassociated Bicorporeality*. Sixty pages
of typescript. A few drawings, and an envelope full of
photos. It is a scientific text and begins with a quote
from Victor Hugo:

"Everyone is free to advance along this dizzying
precipice or to stop and go no further. If you stay still,

you will remain in ordinary life, in ordinary consciousness, with the faith, virtues, and doubts of the common man. If instead you advance, you will be overwhelmed.

"If you insist on grasping what cannot be grasped, if you insist on penetrating the impenetrable, in exploring the inexplorable, then you will launch yourself into the infinite."

Old Hugo is still quite a lion. As I leaf through the manuscript, my eye falls upon this sentence, "We have both a physical corporeality and an areosomatic corporeality, and they may be disassociated from each other." So Leroy is the son of Yram?

The girl's sparkling eyes stare at me, and she bats her eyelashes. I could kiss her. She has unwittingly given me a treasure. I promise to bring her some chocolates next time. Poor girl, with a heavy burden of beauty to bear.

I run to the hotel with the manuscript under my arm. Thank you, Archangel.

I have never found a hotel in Paris which is worth the money you have to pay for it. There is never an armchair to read in, so I lie down on the bed and begin to skim quickly through the manuscript.

Chapter One: Overview of previous research, authors, bibliography. Biometry by Baradouc (1887, very out of date). N Rays by Blanchot and Charpentier (very much discussed in 1903, then all interest faded after 1910). The experiences of De Rochas and Hector Durville (interesting and reliable). The books by the other Durville (Henri, rather a charlatan at times), Lancelin's work (a thick, confused book), Bozzano (detailed, but limited), de Boni (excellent), and Myers (a great work, a classic).

Chapter Two: Five years of research carried out by a group in Paris. Five men and two women. Aim: the transition from physical corporeality to another corporeality which they call Aerosomatic. This aerosoma may provoke phenomena of coloured phosphorescence when placed in front of a screen of calcium sulphide. Under special circumstances it may be photographed. Aerosoma: another name among many. This is something that man has been talking about for thousands of years. There have been many names: Chinese, Indian, Mayan. The Egyptians called it "the double", and the Greeks called it "Psyche" or butterfly because it fluttered. The Christian gnostics called it Pneuma, or air, because it is weightless, the medieval alchemists called it volatile mercury. A century ago they named it the odic body, the astral body, the etheric body, and today these Paris researchers have named it aerosoma.

Chapter Three: The subjects of these experiments, from age thirty to seventy-five, were all in excellent physical and mental health, all regularly employed, including an electronics expert, a laser technician, an engineer, an actuary, a chemist, and the headmaster of a secondary school. The oldest and the director of the group was a doctor, a university professor. During their five years of experiments, one of them began to show signs of mental strain, and had to be replaced. (I must find them. I must get to know them. I'll wait for Denise to come back. I want to meet them face to face and hear their voices. These are the entronauts I have been looking for. Please Archangel, I mean, thank you, Archangel.)

Chapter Four: Physical and psychic preparation from a period of six months to two years. Breathing exercises and techniques for lucid dreaming. The findings of the English researcher Dunne (precognition) and the

Russian Kassatkin (forewarnings of illness). Techniques to interrupt the flow of thoughts while waking and successive voluntary and conscious disassociation. The similarity of the seven experiences compared. Aerosoma near the physical body and distant from it. Aerosomatic zones and their aspects. Beyond aerosoma. Mensoma and Hypersoma.

Here the manuscript ends. Who is Arthur Leroy, the author? I have never heard of him. I will wait for Denise to return. I reread the quotation from Victor Hugo. It seems rather like a warning intended for me personally. You are free to advance or to stand still here on this dizzying precipice. Free? No, I will not turn back. I am very familiar with the common virtues and vices, and they are no longer enough for me.

Denise answers the phone. No one has ever wanted her as much as I do at this moment. A capable woman, still very attractive, and as busy as a minister. She gives me the run down in two minutes. "Arthur Leroy does not exist. It is a collective name for the seven people. They are the Leroys. No, we do not intend to publish the manuscript. I asked someone to lend it to me because I knew you were coming to Paris. It's Yram's subject matter, isn't it? I have found no further information concerning Yram. You say you would like to meet this group. That won't be easy. They are very closed and flee from the indiscreet. You are very indiscreet, no, don't deny it. They will publish their findings in three years, but for the moment, nothing. How can I help you? One of the group has asked me to publish a book of his in our history series. I'll try to bribe him. My secretary sends her regards. She is still waiting for her chocolates, you old dog. As soon as I find out something, I'll call you."

Paris is the capital of the idler – who must have a passive soul and a pair of restless legs. Wandering ascetic, he renounces the *cordon bleu* and contents himself with a bit of bread and *jambon*, accompanied by a mug of beer. Then out into the streets again, in the crowd, in the shops, at the flea market until evening. If he gets hungry suddenly, he buys some fruit from a stall and walks along slowly in the twilight, spitting out the seeds.

In my wandering I revisit those places once frequented by my favourite writers. The Jardin du Luxembourg where Maurice Magre used to come. It was in his pages that I first came to know Pondicherry. A lovely garden, peopled by arguing students, and distracted professors, where young children play, tended by lovely and serious young girls absorbed in books. Perhaps Magre used to sit over there on that isolated bench. Shy, not old but weary, composing in his mind his book of certitude. Each one of us possesses his marvellous certainties.

Rue de Grenelle, where I find the shade of Maurice Maeterlinck, accompanied by his bulldog, on the way to deliver his latest work to his publisher, Fasquelle, full of questions as usual, which he could not answer. The important thing is to ask oneself questions continually .

Montmartre, frequented by boxers; La Villette, homeland of the French bulldog. Rue Volta, where the oldest house in Paris is located at number three, where they say that Descartes once lived, the author of that deadly phrase, "I think, therefore I am". Rather, it should have been, "I am, therefore I think" as the Leroy manuscript clearly shows: they interrupt their thoughts, they stop thinking and yet they are.

Denise telephones, "Tomorrow you will have your

first encounter with a member of the group, but not one of the original seven. Invite him to lunch."

Very good indeed. I get ready to take notes.

Notes taken that evening after the first encounter:

A distinguished fellow, long and lean, very bald for his thirty-five years, and extremely haughty. His arrogance serves him as a shield.

He explains to me as he spreads his napkin. "I am number eight, first on the waiting list. I'll tell you straight away that they have asked me to examine you. I will also add that I am Jewish, so you won't choose any wrong subjects to discuss. Jewish and antisemitic. What about you?"

I try to get him to tell me about the Leroys, but I am not successful.

"You live in Rome. Ecumenicalism. Very interesting. I do not understand why Christians today worry so much about famine. They should be more worried about hell. Dying of hunger is probably the best way of gaining entrance to Paradise. Think of the fasts of the saints. So why should we combat hunger? During the Middle Ages, nothing was done to combat it. I am afraid that today's Christians have become far too materialistic. One moment of hunger down here and we are granted eternal paradise. There is no comparison. Instead of offering food to people, we should take it away from them. Don't you agree? Nobody worries about hell. Do you ever think about it? Hell with its atrocious tortures inhabited by billions of men, women, and children, from all times, doomed to remain there for ever and ever throughout eternity. Every day millions of people join them: our fathers, mothers, children, benefactors, our poets, thinkers, and artists. The best of us, and all those who are not Christians, that is nearly everyone, do you realize the universal horror of it? The Christians should group together: all of them, patriarchs, archbishops, abbots, priests, pastors, monks, ministers, and nuns, the hundreds of millions of the faithful, unite their efforts across the globe and pray night and day, moaning, crying, imploring Jesus to open up the gates of hell and liberate the suffering. Before such cries, Jesus would surely forgive them and give us a sign. Hell and not hunger. I am afraid that Christians today are too materialistic."

I reply, "Jesus has already done that. After the resurrection, he descended into hell, then ascended into heaven, and he was not alone."

He is astonished, "Do you think one divine descent into hell is enough to obliterate it?"

He wants to shock me and he has succeeded. He wants to keep me from asking questions and this tactic has worked. He eats hardly anything: he is a vegetarian and a teetotaller.

"No, not by choice. I am a connoisseur of champagne and caviar. But I have been in training for a year now. What was that name you called us, 'Entronauts'? Boxers need to eat steaks, not vegetables. You are interested in our experiments, aren't you?"

Finally he opens up. He admits that he knows nothing from firsthand experience. He follows Hamlet's belief, "Everything is possible." "If it is truly possible to leave one's body and be conscious in the aerosoma, then everything changes, all our values change, our concepts of life and death. Do you agree? Our great reluctance towards the idea of immortality depends on our inability to conceive the soul without a body. But you must speak to those who have had the experience of that detachment." He smiles and becomes friendlier.

"I know I must die and I feel that I cannot, so I have become involved in this undertaking. Perhaps death is only life, as yet misunderstood."

Outside the restaurant, he excuses himself. "Have I offended your Christian soul? This is an era in which men may judge their gods."

He leaves. I have discovered nothing. He has examined me.

Notes from the next evening, after the second encounter. I seem to have passed the first test.

Lunch again, but with a different man. He seems older than the first, because of his grey hair, yet he is not. Shorter, sturdier, athletic. He is not as eloquent as the other. He reflects, searches for the right words, then falls silent. We both seem rather awed by the subject which so intrigues us, and so we barely touch on it. Mutual trust cannot be improvised. For Maggie, it would be easy, her heart knows how to bless everyone in silence. Blessing opens the doors within.

Lunch passes quickly, all in vain. I suggest we take a walk in the Jardin du Luxembourg, hoping that the lawns, flowers, and trees may help us relax. As we walk, I tell him the story of my search. Sam with his nudism, the scientists in the monastery, Essy with her peyote, Maggie with her omnipotence, the providential Denise. My search for Yram led me to the Leroys. Through a charming and silly secretary.

We sit down. His grey hair contrasts with his fresh, tan face. He begins to speak.

It is a binding and total experience, like the training before a world championship is for an athlete. Day and night, rather night and day. We must open a crack in our consciousness, prisoners as we are of our corporeal senses. We begin with sleep and waking, when disassociation occurs naturally. It is a long, hard, technical task requiring perseverance. Slowly, slowly consciousness passes lucidly from waking to sleep. Then another crack must be opened in the mind.

When we are not imprisoned in our senses, we are imprisoned in the mind.

He is silent, perhaps he is tired of talking, perhaps it is difficult for him. I remember what Essy had to say about peyote. "The mind becomes weightless and our thoughts fade, but not our awareness. Thoughts vanish, the last ones leave very slowly, like distant birds flying through the sky. Then an overwhelming silence."

I repeat aloud, "an overwhelming silence".

He looks surprised, "Yes," he says.

He is silent. Along the paths we encounter argumentative students, distracted professors, children tended by lovely, serious girls with their books. He is silent.

Now and then we become aware of the twittering birds. He looks at me and smiles, and then picks up where he left off.

"Once we have conquered dream, we are ready for detachment during waking. Detachment, utter astonishment. Suddenly you find yourself standing in your room, among your familiar objects, feeling weightless. You look around at your table, your bookcase, your couch. There is someone on the couch . . . Who is it? A man asleep . . . No, that's me . . . My body. A horror seizes you, terrible and lacerating. So I am dead, you say. Mother, please no, I have so many things to do. They need me. Your long preparation now comes to your aid. You are not dead, you are simply disassociated. Indeed, you have a second body. The aerosoma, smaller, lighter, free from gravity, propelled by will power. One body tied to the other by means of a luminous, coloured vibrating link, almost like an umbilical cord. The horror slowly fades, replaced by a deep desire to know. You observe, compare, verify. The fact of our bicorporeal reality becomes evident and undeniable. You observe and verify and compare and realize that the values of your life have been shattered. Life is not what we have always believed it to be. It is completely different."

More students and professors pass by along the paths. The birds are still singing. As he says goodbye to me, he concludes: "Perhaps the men of the future will tell tales of our times, when people still believed in death."

Notes from the next evening, after the third and last encounter.

An elderly man, the head of the group, invited me to his home.

"Entronauts. I like the word. Did you coin it?"

He is a tall and lean old man with white hair. A large Adam's apple protrudes from his wizened throat and bobs up and down as he talks. Incredible pale blue eyes above gaunt cheeks. Those eyes stare deep into mine and I can feel their vibration, as gentle as his voice.

"We will publish everything in three years, I believe. Please don't write too much about us. It would be a good idea if you gave us back the manuscript, don't you think? You are planning to go to Persia, India, the Far East. Good for you. They told me about your physicists in California, and about your peyote. We avoid all stimulants, including coffee, tea, wine, and animal protein. We use our consciousness, we change it from a liquid to a solid state."

He is an old man who immediately wins your trust and affection. You feel that he has gone a long way, and that he has seen, experienced, and understood many things.

"We will publish everything, perhaps. My friend, it may seem incredible, but it isn't. Reaching the aerosoma is easy for those who are in good health, who are well balanced, psychologically fit, well prepared and guided. You only have to strengthen your consciousness and give it greater continuity, so that it doesn't fall into the habitual oblivion of the morning after, when you wake from your dream, the oblivion of Lazarus after his resurrection. It only seems incredible to us because they have hammered that old lie into our heads: 'but no one has ever come back to tell us what it is like.' But that is not true at all. From time immemorial, men have been leaving and coming back to tell us what they have experienced. Read their poetry, read history. Restless Ulysses who travelled the world over: mountains, oceans, poles, the equator, beneath the earth and beneath the sea, in the skies, throughout the cosmos. Don't you think he was tempted to cross this threshold? If not, then you do not know him."

He gets up, takes a bottle, and offers me a sort of elixir. I quite warm to this old man. He seems so fragile, so ephemeral, so rare.

"But perhaps we won't publish our findings. The aerosoma is only the first phase. After the first astonishing experiences, it becomes easier to swing back and forth between these two dimensions at will. Restless Ulysses is not satisfied with contemplating his body on the couch. He discovers that the aerosoma has its own space where it may travel. He discovers that there is yet another dimension beyond the second one: Mensoma? And beyond that, yet another. Hypersoma? What language exists to describe this reality? We have gone beyond the mind, beyond the expressible, more so than your Californian physicists. Drink, drink, you will like it."

He gets up from his chair and points at the bookcase with his long bony arm. "What language shall we use? We have tried to use a scientific one. You have seen the manuscript. But it is too limited. Other languages, far more expressive, have been used in the past: the language of symbols, of poetry, of magic, religion, alchemy. Perhaps alchemy attained the greatest capacity for communication. We Leroys have a very impoverished language. We reach the Aerosoma and stop there. But what about all the rest?"

And what would that be?

He stares at me with his pale blue eyes, no longer gentle, but vigorous and penetrating in their attempt to be more eloquent than words.

"Your American Indian girl, your peyote girl was telling the truth. Not all of our soul is incarnate. She was right: the universe is a sublime vibration of joy. And pain? A momentary dissonant, ripple."

JOURNEY TO PERSIA

Few people know what the director is really like, and those who know keep silent. Most people think of him as a journalist who directs. In reality he is a despot who commands. Tyrant of variable moods, one day he will scream at you for the slightest error, and smile the next day at a fatal mistake. A tyrant whose tastes remain a mystery, who is prone to incomprehensible and abrupt decisions. My father used to say: don't sit up front in an automobile, don't sit in back on a horse, with your director neither sit in front nor in back. I know newspaper directors very well. For the last thirty years they have been giving me my bread. So I don't eat very much, because I try to avoid them.

After I had left Paris and was back in Rome again, I found myself facing a dilemma. I was either going to have to capture a director and convince him to send me on assignment, or abandon my idea. Directors are big game, and difficult to hunt. There is a technique, yet it isn't easy, even less so than it used to be, since I no longer have Edoardo to help me.

What had I accomplished in New York, London, Los Angeles, Paris? Nothing, nothing at all. Yes, I had discovered the cult of peyote, but it's not for me. Besides I am excluded, only Indians may be admitted and I am a pale face. Yes, I found Maggie and omnipotence, and she gave me an Archangel. But I want much more than that. I want to become the Archangel myself, to share its blessedness and its immortality. Yes, I had found the Leroys but what's the use of moving from an earthly drama to another subtler and more incomprehensible one if we remain only actors on the stage? I want to go behind the wings and discover who is directing the performance, who decides the births and deaths. The death of the people I love, my own death. I want to read the script. Or I want to find out once and for all that there is no script and no director.

Three years ago I began my research and I must bring it to conclusion. There are people in the world who claim that they have met God face to face and that they speak with him. I must find these people and either unmask them or kneel down before them. Who are they? The Sufis of Islam, the lamas of Tibet, the bonzos of Siam, the Sadhus of India, ninety-year-old Mère of Pondicherry, and the eighty-six-year-old Japanese master Uyeshiba of Tokyo. And the great anchorites of Mt. Athos.

"You're a bit mad, really a bit mad."

A sweet woman says this to me. She is not very intelligent and yet she knows me better than I know myself. I often meet intelligent men and women at receptions, famous professors and academics. But their conversation is very boring. This pains me because I would like to admire them. But they only talk about themselves or speak unkindly of others, or tell jokes. I would like to ask them some essential questions, but as I look at them (friendly and smiling with a glass in hand and their admirers gathered around them) I realize that not only is it the wrong place and time, but they are definitely the wrong people to ask.

You're a bit mad, really a bit mad.

She must be right. If I were not mad, I would probably be rich and famous and if I were rich and famous, I would probably not feel the need to search, and so I would not need to capture some director.

The first rule for capturing directors is not to follow them. If you follow them, you are lost. If you present yourself to a director and openly tell him about your idea to go in search of entronauts, he will reply.

"Entronauts? What are those?"

"You know, inner continents."

"But what continents are you talking about?"

Here he has disarmed you. He is no longer your prey, you are his. Indeed he announces:

"I want you to go to Vigevano. Do you know how important shoes are? You must write me an article about the shoe industry. It's not easy. That's why I want you to do it."

If you don't escape immediately, the next day you may find yourself in Vigevano.

So then, the first rule: don't go looking for him. Second rule, let him come to you.

For this you need a middleman, someone like Edoardo. But he's off in the Congo. Someone who, as if by chance, says to him:

"I just ran into so and so. Remember him? He's done some articles for us. He told me about an article he's writing. Something really big."

The director, curious, "Who's he doing it for?"

"He's not sure yet. Maybe . . ."

"Call him and tell him I want to see him."

You've won the first battle. Your prey is now on your trail. The next battle is the face-to-face confrontation. The director sits behind his huge table, and though he is sitting down he seems to be standing straight and tall, looming over you. He says, "I haven't seen you for years. Why is that? Don't you feel like writing any more? Got any good ideas?"

I've got one, but it would require a lot of travelling to many different places: Greece, Persia, India, Siam, China, Japan, and back again. It would be an exhausting trip, so I don't know. . .

"What's your idea?"

"Not dying."

"Not dying?"

"Not dying."

"Not dying?"

"Becoming immortal."

"Explain yourself."

Third rule: have an outline ready, in other words, a summary of your idea in twenty lines: concise, clever, ready in your pocket. I hand him the paper and he reads it silently. Your fate is being determined in that silence. I address my Archangel, "Take care of this for me, please, will you?"

He looks up at you and says yes. That's right, he says yes. Then he announces, "I want you on the next plane to Tehran."

I listen to him without either astonishment or joy. My clever tactics suddenly seem petty and futile. This journey was my destiny, though I don't know since when or why. The dialogue with the director has been a simple formality, a visa in my passport. I am overwhelmed by the certainty that everything is determined beforehand: my proposal and his saying yes. The lines were written in the script. But who is the author?

As we descend Tehran appears below the plane. The sun is setting behind the mountains, fading on the plain, vanishing amid the bright lights of the city.

I look down at that knot of streets, alleys, and avenues stretching on and on and feel defeated. How will I ever find the way, the right path to travel, the right doors to knock on in order to meet the men I am looking for? I am looking for the Sufis, but where are they hiding? Because Sufis conceal themselves from public view. They have always done so.

The Sufi is an initiate in search of wisdom, holiness, and perfection. He searches, suffers, and then at last finds what he is seeking. For others, he leads a scandalous existence. He rejects our brief pleasures, our petty powers. He stays still, while we whirl in the dance of life: tears and laughter, delight and fear. Today alive, but dead tomorrow. We cannot tolerate his serene smile. For the last twelve centuries he has hidden from us, blessing us in silence. If he reveals himself, they will kill him. Throughout history, Sufis have been the victims of murder.

They killed Ali, the purest example of the Sufi, the companion of Mohammed. They plunged a dagger in his heart while he was immersed in inner contemplation. They killed Bistani while he was filled with the spirit and singing its praises. They whipped, mutilated, and hanged Hallag, and then decapitated him, and scattered his ashes. The dark cannot tolerate the illuminated.

While I descend the ramp of the plane I feel very disheartened. How will I ever find them?

You're a bit mad, really a bit mad.

She is right. I have given my word to the director. I have chosen the first stop, Persia, and I have arrived in Tehran and I do not know where to go or what to do. The city is enormous and no one knows me. It will be hard enough to find a hotel, much less find Sufis to talk with. I really must be mad.

I wait in line at passport control and customs. Suddenly the loudspeaker announces my name, yes my name, and repeats it. It adds in English that they are waiting for me.

I may be mad, but I have an Archangel.

It was no miracle of the Sufis. There is no word for "miracle" in the language of the Koran. Instead of miracle they say, "sign". My name being called on the loudspeaker is, if you like, a sign. If not, you may consider it a friend's kindness. I had told a friend of mine in Rome (who had come to show me a bulldog – as I am an expert on the subject of bulldogs) about my trip to Persia. He is in the oil business, but I don't know exactly what he does. We only talk about bulldogs. Unknown to me, he sent a message to his agents here and they have rushed to the airport to welcome me.

There are two of them, both Italians and they call me "professor". I'd like to tell them that I am not a professor, but I wouldn't want to disappoint them. They take my bags, put me in a car, inform me that they have already made my hotel arrangements, and invite me out to dinner. I begin to realize that my friend in the oil business is a very important man.

At dinner we discuss the weather. For four months out of the year, Persia is swept by an enervating wind which stifles all impulse to do anything. For the rest of the time, work is always against nature, because it tires you so. Next we discuss oil. They explain the problems of the business which are quite obscure to me.

Then they ask me why I have come here. They are two very pleasant fellows, in their mid-thirties, one an engineer, the other a geologist. Their world is made up of drilling, refineries, and pipelines. They are convinced that these are important things, the only important things. When I remark that from the times of Adam until yesterday, man achieved greatness without oil, they just laugh, thinking that it's a joke. The geologist repeats the question, "Are you here to do an article? How can we help you?"

My friend, you don't know how much I need help. But how can I tell you that I am unable to write about oil, economics, sociology or politics. You'd think I was a good-for-nothing (and you'd be right) and you would think less of my friend in Rome. I really need help, but I have to tell you, "I'm looking for Sufis."

There, I said it (though I don't know how I found the courage). Both of them look at me, full of enthusiasm. So I add, "Suf is the fleece mantle that the ancient Sufis used to wear and it smelt like a wet sheep. In Persia they are also called dervishes, in Arabia fakir, in Africa Marabout, names which remind us of Salgari, but perhaps you haven't read him, since you belong to another generation. Dervishes, fakirs, marabouts . . . pejorative translations because of the ancient misunderstanding between Christians and Muslims, dating back to the time of the Crusades. So there you have it, friends, I'm looking for the Sufis.

They are dear friends indeed because they are not stopped by this mysterious word, by this mysterious quest. I would give up entirely if they should ask me something about the search for oil in the Persian Gulf. But no, they consult each other, then the engineer goes to make a phone call and the geologist says, "Perhaps we'll find a way."

They do. The engineer returns.

There's a professor at the university involved in these things. His name is Ruzbehan. Tomorrow he is giving a lecture at the university. We'll send a car to your hotel.

The hotel is excellent, the room comfortable, my heart is lightened. Why should I doubt my Archangel? I only need to entrust myself to him and say thank you.

The University of Tehran is quite new. At the centre is the mosque, a place of prayer. The Persian mosque is open to the sky and flooded with light. There are no priests or deacons. Islam rejected clergy, rituals, hierarchies, patriarchs, like Hinduism, Taoism, Judaism, Shinto, Manicheism, and the Celts. It was Late Roman times, a period tainted by paganism, which introduced the idea of the Pope to Christianity, in a marriage of the sacred and profane. Islam requires only prayer and fasting. No images adorn the walls of the mosque, only verses of the Koran.

I wander from building to building and finally find the secretary's office where they explain everything to me. Ruzbehan is a doctor and psychiatrist, and this morning he will address the international conference on the unity of science. His talk is entitled *The Brain and Consciousness*.

My hopes fall. Conferences are forums of vanity, the unity of the sciences is a fantasy, psychiatry possesses no certainty and gives none.

All the same, I go into the hall, sit in a corner and listen to Ruzbehan and soon I take out my notebook and begin taking notes. This Persian psychiatrist has some astonishing things to say to this conference of scientists. But most of them are chatting or dozing. I seem to be the only one paying attention.

". . . man uses only two or three tenths of the connections and circuits present in his brain (Penfield) . . . brain area 19, mute and silent (Boardmann) . . . we have not five but twenty senses (Martin): the sense of balance, orientation, space, time, vibration of our emotions, psychic resonance with others, the seizing of a passing thought in the mind . . . all these perceptions quite common in us go beyond the limits of the ordinary senses and open to us an immense knowledge."

Ruzbehan continues to read his paper, simultaneously translated into four languages, and yet hardly anyone is listening. In the audience small groups discuss the distribution of teaching positions and invite each other to future conferences, shamelessly exemplifying *do ut des*.

"Over the last century, science has modified the mental image man has of himself . . . the exclusive importance given to the five conventional senses has caused people to have in their minds an image of themselves which is corporeal and nothing more, forgetting the reality furnished by our non-conventional senses. This has had disastrous consequences. Our mistaken cerebral image of ourselves as a body leads the individual to anguish and falsifies his behaviour, which has dangerous consequences for society as we may plainly see all around us . . . "

I close the notebook. Ruzbehan is someone to get to know, but not here, even though I don't like his confusing the mind with the brain, or rather the musician with the instrument. He should read Bergson. I go out of the hall and leave the university, and stroll through the streets of Tehran. It is a city without parks, with red double-decker buses, orange taxis, traffic policemen with oriental caps, and white donkeys. The donkey is the companion of poor people. He eats little, is always working and can be found everywhere. Wherever you find donkeys, you find poverty. You find them in Lucania, but not in Lombardy. Throughout the canton of Berne, there is only one donkey – at the zoo.

Persian women do not cover their faces though they are Muslims. Instead, they wear a long veil from head to toe, through which their miniskirts can be glimpsed. Their veils render them secret and desirable.

In the morning while shaving, I look at my face in the mirror and do not recognize it. It seems to me the face of some sort of anthropoid, though not human, and decidedly not my own face. A normal face, an ordinary face, not ugly perhaps. There are some people who like it and others who love it. Not me. It is foreign to me. I do not have a corporeal image of myself in my brain.

In my case Professor Ruzbehan would seem to be wrong, though actually he is right. Most people think of themselves as a body and nothing else. Fatal consequences result in the fields of economics, politics, art, and social behaviour. Because of that image, religion has lost its power, literature despairs, sex dominates. A simple, mental image, impalpable, invisible, subjective, something so insignificant and yet it determines present and future destinies. If it were changed, everything else would change.

I must meet this Ruzbehan. My friends in the oil business take care of this for me and try to make him believe that I am a journalist who has come to Tehran to interview him. They play the card of vanity.

This fails. The professor sends a copy of his talk to me at my hotel along with a polite note, saying that everything he has to say may be found in his paper.

Touché. I deserved the lesson, why should I try to approach those on high from below, from their presumed defects and not their virtues?

I have been wounded, but not beaten. I'll go to him as a patient and pay for the visit. But I must see him.

From close to, Ruzbehan's face seems dominated by his nose, which is very prominent as in most Persians. But soon the importance of the nose fades, thanks to his friendly smile. When I meet his eyes I see nothing else: large, dark, immobile, interrogatory, heavy to bear. They compel me to tell him the truth. I am the journalist come from Europe but not to interview him. I heard him speak at the university, I read his conference paper and I want to speak to him. He may consider me a patient, if he so wishes. A woman who knows me very well claims that I am mad. She is probably right.

He laughs and leaves his place behind the big desk, invites me to sit in an armchair, while he sits in the other. Tea is brought and he offers me a cigarette. Thanks, but I don't smoke. (Actually, I smoke a pipe, but when I left for the East I promised myself that I would abstain from tobacco, alcohol, and women.)

"What is the aim of your journey?"

I would like to keep things vague, but his eyes will not allow me. They are too big, too resolute, too penetrating, too heavy to bear if you do not tell the truth.

I answer, somewhat confused. Not to die, this is the aim. Everyone accepts that we must die, everyone tries not to think about it, and in the end everyone dies. Not dying almost seems to be a refusal to accept life as it is, day in day out, petty, selfish, hypocritical, a cattle market, *do ut des*. To look for another inner atmosphere, a cause to dedicate those few days which have been granted us. Years ago in India I met some men and women living in perfect joy, who irradiated serenity. My aim is not to live as I do, swallowed up by hours, days, season and years, by the future which soon becomes the past and then vanishes for ever. My aim?

To discover if the promises are true or only a hoax. To discover if Krishna was lying when he spoke of eternal joy, if Buddha was lying when he claimed that he had found immortality, if Jesus was lying about eternal life, if Mohammed was lying . . .

Here I stop. Ruzbehan is a Muslim and I am offending him. What I wanted to say is all tangled up. I try to save myself with a smile, "In London I found an Archangel".

He nods in approval. "Archangels are powerful."

Back in the hotel, I note down some of the things he said to me. He is more than a scientist. Scientist, science, scientific seem to me depreciatory terms. We all know that they have the destruction of mankind ready in their laboratories. The method of the sciences is inhuman: on one hand they give you refrigerators and penicillin, and on the other hand wholesale massacres. It is inhuman, but it forces us to honour each year the inventors of the atomic bomb – science, mad tyrant, *morituri te salutant*.

Ruzbehan said, "Our century is very different from all previous ones because for the last hundred years the human brain has been utilized in a new way, which has brought us modern technology. New connections, new channels have been made in the neurons, but the old ones, the ancient ones have been closed. In dedicating ourselves only to profane sciences, we have obliterated the mental circuits which belong to the sacred sciences. Those are introspective sciences, but introspection is rigorously experimental. The sacred exists, and if it ceases to be a part of man's life, he grows pale, anaemic, and desolate."

Then he concluded cordially, "You have come here to cure your anaemia."

The encounter was coming to an end and I had not yet mentioned the Sufis. Overcoming my reserve, I murmured, "Do you think the Sufis can heal me?"

He did not answer, as though he had not heard. But this morning I received a note, "Here is an address. You will be welcomed."

No Persian Sufi calls himself by that name. He will call his master a Sufi, but for himself he will use the word dervish, or beggar, the beggar of Allah. Allah is God, the highest, the absolute.

The Sufi is a beggar who does not beg, and one would never tell by his appearance that he belongs to an order of initiates – he is a shopkeeper, a workman, a university professor, a technician, a fruitseller, a peasant.

He has a wife and children and is very busy. But his real business is his inner world. He lives like everyone else, and yet he is different. We are immersed in our actions, swallowed up by them. He keeps a short distance between himself and his actions and leans on Allah.

I know everything about the Sufis. I have been to visit them and they have opened their doors to welcome me, thanks to Ruzbehan's introduction. I can tell you that there are various Sufi schools in Persia. The three most important ones are: Nematollah, which traces itself back to Ali; Zakhabi, a less spiritual school, and Khaxar in which the dervishes are easily recognizable because they wear rags and live by begging, and withdraw to the mountains to commune with Allah.

A Nematollah master said to me:

"Close to God is the great ascetic who lives in the world and builds a mountain in his heart."

I asked him, "What is Sufism?"

He shrugged his shoulders, "Anything you can say about Sufism, is not Sufism."

He is right. It's not true that I know everything about Sufis. In reality, I know nothing. But I am slowly discovering something.

My pilgrimage among the dervishes begins at one of their meetings in a place located in the outskirts of Tehran. I am welcomed by the master, a very pleasant man, a merchant by trade. I am not allowed to take part in their meeting, but I may be admitted to the library which houses two hundred ancient manuscripts. The Master's name is Ahmad. For him, Sufis are love-sick poets.

In the days that follow, I attend another meeting at another place in Tehran, with another master, a mineralogist by profession. He smiles little, and is of few words. His name is Karim. For him, Sufis are spiritual technicians.

My pilgrimage takes me from Tehran to Isfahan, the ancient capital, where I meet two Sufi masters, a fruitseller and a custodian. The first one is named Zarkub, and he belongs to the school of the dancing dervishes. He is a lively and pugnacious man, an actor. For him Sufis are dancers.

The custodian tends the tomb of a famous dervish who died fifty years ago. He is a silent old man. His name is Tarmadi. Below his bushy eyebrows, I discover the charming gaze of a child. When I ask him, "What is a Sufi?" he answers reflectively, "Someone who has departed."

So is the Sufi a poet, a technician, a dancer, or an absentee? Perhaps he is all of these things, a complex knot which must be unravelled with great patience. I am not very patient and my memory is not very good.

Now, as I write, a few months after my encounter, I seem to be confusing the four masters – not completely (since Zarkub's moustache is too evident and Tarmadi is too silent to mistake them one for the other), but I seem to have got their words mixed up. Looking back at my notes, I no longer remember who said what.

I remember very well that Ahmad spoke about love, and that he cited the great Persian poets, "All Sufis, all Sufis". Among his two hundred manuscripts, he always managed to find the verses which illustrated whatever point he was trying to make. From those verses a striking image of the dervish emerged: a pilgrim if not a vagabond, in love with wine and with woman, and yet sometimes so drunk with Allah that he forgets to put on his clothes, like Taher, known as the naked one. Mad with God, and rejecters of the world, in which they do not seek glory but scorn, like Garmani who in order to seem ignoble after his death, left a scandalous testament for teetotal Islam: "Wash my corpse with wine, give the coffin to two drunkards, bury it near the tavern, there where the boozers vomit."

Woman is always at the heart of the dervish's life, even in old age. "Why does your adolescent gaze tremble before me, old man? Why does a young love invade my grey head? Come, entwine your black locks amid my white hair, my night and your day united will ignite the dawn."

And finally a quotation from Molana; among the great he is the greatest, Molana whose ecstasies were so deep they seemed like death: "Who is the intimate being who dwells in my eye and looks out? Who is hidden behind the pupil of my eye? We are only a gaze, the rest is absence."

I cannot remember either the face of Ahmad or Karim. If I met them on the street, I would not recognize them. My only clear memory of the first is his two hundred manuscripts, and of the second, his four hats. I can see them so clearly in my mind that I could paint them. They were always on his table: the hat Karim wore when he was wearing his dervish robes, the second was the hat which his master had given him, the third belonged to the master of his master, and the fourth belonged to an ancient sage dating back to a time no one remembered any longer. The hat is important because it covers the head – rather it is above the head, and indeed it is beyond the head where the Sufi encounters Allah.

I asked Ahmad and Karim:

"Can anyone become a dervish?"

Neither gave me an answer.

Perhaps I have forgotten the faces of Ahmad and Karim because they disappointed me. They were very generous in offering me their hospitality, in giving me information, and even telling me secrets, but they avoided the essential question. I had not gone to Persia in order to seek information, instructions, or pleasure. I had gone there in order to find out at first hand about those questions which troubled me; whatever the price I was willing to risk it, perhaps to fail, or even go mad if I didn't succeed.

There is a point at which Islam becomes truly fascinating. Charles de Foucauld, Catholic saint, understood it. I said to myself that if they possess the truth, then I want to become a dervish, though the suf stinks of wet sheep. But they avoided answering this question.

I will never forget Ruzbehan's face. He helped me like a brother, even as far as the photos were concerned. Articles for magazines must always be accompanied by photos, extraordinary photos which only professional photographers know how to take. So I had to find a good photographer and above all, I had to persuade the Sufis to let me photograph them in costume. A difficult undertaking with people as closed as they are. How could I show up in the places where their ceremonies were to be held, followed by a photographer and all his lighting equipment?

Meanwhile the days in Tehran were speeding by, and my encounters with the masters Ahmad and Karim had come to an end. The problem of obtaining photos was becoming an obsession for me. Restless, I began to reconsider the reasons for my trip. Why had I come to Persia? What had I meant when I told Essy that she must now make her life sacred, and that we must make our hidden sides emerge? Phrases which were obscure even to me, or were perhaps a confused intuition of the truth.

I decided to ask Ruzbehan for advice, not concerning the photos, but concerning my own disappointment. I said to him, "Instead of searching for Sufis or what have you, in other words, seeking one's own salvation, perhaps it would be better to dedicate oneself to a cause, like social reforms or a revolutionary cause. To think about others, like Schweitzer."

The conversation was in French. Ruzbehan speaks an eloquent and cultured French. In his phrasing you can even hear the punctuation: the comma, the paragraph indention, the parentheses, even the underlining:

"You told me last time that in London Maggie had given you certainty: the control room is *inside* us. But we have sought it *outside*. That is why the fall of every Bastille is followed by a Napoleon. Man changes *inside* or he doesn't change at all. Today's great technological revolution has led us to nuclear weapons. Save others?

Yes, by saving ourselves. Elevate others, yes, by elevating ourselves, by changing from the superior animal that we are to the man who is *truly* superhuman. This is what we are all seeking."

I reply, "Superhuman? I am an animal. I only want to find a way not to die completely, I only want to understand a little bit."

"Let me give you some advice. Go to Isfahan. You will find the right man there and your photos as well."

An hour's flight. I leave Tehran, much too contemporary to be beautiful. Beauty is the privilege of young women and ancient cities. I leave Tehran under a full moon. The terraces are full of sleepers for in the summer people sleep outside on their roofs. A million inhabitants lie revealing their nakedness, their dreams, and their loves to the moon.

I fall asleep staring at the golden dome of the great mosque of Tehran glinting silver in the moonlight, and I awake to the sight of the domes of Isfahan's splendid mosques. They remind me of the cathedral domes in the Amalfi peninsula. They are made of blue ceramic and melt into the sky. To the north, Demavend, the most beautiful mountain in the world, a pyramid six thousand metres high, mysterious, the colour of lapis lazuli.

Isfahan has been one of Persia's most splendid cities for the last one thousand years. Here I am seeking the right man, who only speaks Persian, and so I need an interpreter who understands the words of the right man. For this purpose Ruzbehan has given me two letters.

The first man is a professor, but I do not find him at the university, instead a misunderstanding arises with a man whose name is similar, an architect who takes a sudden liking to me but who speaks only English and so we do not understand each other. He loads my bag into his car, makes me get in, and then lets me out at the bridge of twenty-three arches, drags me to the harem of forty columns and then to the Tower, and then the mosques, and on and on. In vain I tell him that I am not interested in seeing the sights, that I am looking for the right man. But he doesn't try to understand me, he simply says yes yes and heads towards the minarets.

I finally free myself abruptly by grabbing my bag before his astonished eyes and running into a hotel. Then I immediately regret what I have done and want to rush after him to beg his pardon, but I cannot waste time. I am looking for the right man.

The second letter is for a fruitseller who has lived in France. His name is Bahar and he understands the words of the right man. I lose my way in the narrow labyrinthine streets until I find his shop: Bahar is away, he is in Tehran. His father is there, who speaks only Persian. I stare at him in defeat.

He is a tall, robust man with a bushy moustache. He smiles at me, and makes me sit on an apple crate, and hands me a bunch of grapes. He chats with his customers (women in veils, darkhaired little boys) points me out to them (who knows who he thinks I am, or what he is saying to them), shows them the letter for his son, but does not read it, though it is written in Persian. He may be illiterate. Between customers he talks to me, raising his voice a bit, because of the popular conviction that strangers who do not understand your language are deaf and so you must raise your voice. He plays the part of a Persian fruitseller very well. I nibble the grapes. And now, poor man? A luminous thought cuts through the dark clouds of my disappointment: the Archangel. I tell him, "Listen, take care of this for me. Thank you."

I remain there squatting on the uncomfortable crate, witnessing the selling of apples, vegetables and salad. Lunchtime comes around and the fruitseller go away, then comes back with his lunch and shares it with me. Lunch consists of boiled rice (*celo* in Persian, Zarkub shouts at me) with mutton (*kabab* in Persian, he shouts). In order to thank him, I repeat *celo*, *kabab*. He smiles, content, and offers me a glass of water.

I don't move. I will wait. By now everything is in the hands of the Archangel.

You're a bit mad, really a bit mad.

Afternoon comes. I can't stand it any more. Not because of the wait, but because of my bladder. A little boy once asked me, "Why is it that people never need to use the bathroom in books?" Who knows if Archangels understand these things?

Zarkub understands however. He takes me by the arm and leads me to the back of the shop, all the while saying, "Bahar Tehran. Tehran!"

I get it, I get it, friend. I am not waiting for Bahar, but for the Archangel.

He asks me, "Italian?"

"Yes, yes, Italian or almost. How can I tell you that in Switzerland there are three tribes?"

He leaves the shop. People come to buy and ask me questions. I smile and they serve themselves and leave the money on the counter. Half an hour passes, forty minutes. What is happening? I don't worry too much. It's the Archangel's business.

Then Zarkub reappears with a little girl. Actor that he is, he bursts out in a mimed explanation, repeating, "Italian, Italian," several times.

Then the little girl speaks. "*Bon giorno*. My mother Italian."

I am astonished. Archangel, you are remarkable.

A little girl of about thirteen, very thin with long black plaits, quite plain except for her eyes. Her name is Simine. She wears a veil over her dress, as if she were a woman, though she is not. Her Italian is very broken. Is this the interpreter? And yet if the Archangel has chosen her, she must be the person I need.

In fact she immediately frees me from my verbal prison. She is intelligent – you can tell by her eyes when I speak to her. She wrinkles her forehead until she has understood my sentence, and then illuminated, fervent, she translates for Zarkub. A very essential dialogue emerges, like the ones which must have transpired between the Amerinds and the pale faces.

"I come Isfahan to see master Tarmadi, Sufi."

I get up and pick up Ruzbehan's letter which has been left lying among the fruits and vegetables, and I say, "Zarkub read letter".

Zarkub reads and answers.

"I am not master Tarmadi, I Zarkub, dervish."

"You dervish?"

"Dervish."

At last I am no longer deafmute. Simine, I would kiss you if I weren't afraid that my gesture might be misunderstood. Zarkub. Zarkub is not only a dancer, he is a master. He belongs to the order of the Mevlevi, the dancing dervishes. Tall, robust, proud, moustachioed, fruitseller and crate carrier, he has nothing in common with the effeminate dancer that we know in the West. His dancing is something very different from our own. Simine translates for me.

"You dervish dancer. How you dance?"

"Like David."

"Which David?"

"King."

King David danced before the Ark, filled with

Jehovah. That is how the Mevlevi dance, filled with Allah.

I have seen the dervishes dance. Zarkub arranged it for me. I watched them during the still silent night, hidden in a dark corner of the terrace outside the illuminated room where the dervishes were holding their meeting.

I should not write about it. Not that anyone has imposed silence on me. I should not write about it because the written word cannot recreate the magic of music or dance. What words can describe Bach? Who can describe Allah penetrating the hearts of his devoted? Not even the Bible succeeds: "David danced before the Lord with all his might, singing to the sounds of tabrets. And David was filled with the spirit of the Lord." This says everything, and nothing.

Before trying to describe it in writing, I should clean my tool: the word. For us dancing is the boredom of classical ballet, or the whirling chaos of savages, or the subhuman thrashing about of discos. But there is also the dance of the wind, which we see in the trees, the invisible dance of the hours, the dance of the angels, and the arcane dance of the universe, and sometimes during nights of insomnia we hear the music of the spheres.

Before describing it, I should eliminate a few superstitions. The superstition that the word "self-suggestion" explains everything. In reality this word is only a useless label which means nothing. The superstition that by twirling your head, you get dizzy, and that David mistook this dizziness for the holy spirit. I would like to eliminate the great superstition that reduces us to one dimension: the dimension of the body. This is worse than a superstition; it is amnesia.

If I could do this, then I could describe the dance of the dervishes. But I don't know how to do it, and yet I saw the dervishes dance.

The dance began late at night. It was preceded by a very long silence. Crouching in that dark, hidden corner of the terrace, barely breathing, I could see clearly the seven dervishes in the brightly lit room. They wore antique clothes and hats, red, yellow, and white, and they had brought out their ritual objects along with their musical instruments. The room was filled with an oriental incense which perhaps was wafting up from below, or out from the room, or perhaps was inside me. The sky slowly filled with stars.

Zarkub read or recited, I don't know which. Verses from the Koran, or poetry, or magic words? His voice reached me as pure sound, without meaning. Then it stopped and there followed another long silence.

Dhekr or *fana*. *Dhekr* is the repetition of a divine name. *Fana* is silent contemplation. In my dialogue with Zarkub I had asked him, through Simine, the veiled child, "Please, think about me in your prayers."

This confused him, and he excused himself, acting a bit, as usual. "Impossible, impossible. When there is *fana*, Zarkub is no longer here."

It was deep night and in the dark I watched the seven dervishes sitting cross-legged on the floor, immobile. Then I heard a few strains of music and Zarkub got up. The night was sacred, the room was sacred, the firmament was sacred. How can I describe them? "David danced before the Lord with all his might, singing to the sounds of tabrets. And David was filled with the spirit of the Lord."

I saw such a thing take place before me – the distant spectator.

Zarkub led me to master Tarmadi. Zarkub (proud,

moustachioed, a gesticulating actor) was so accommodating to me that he made me feel guilty. He allowed me to photograph him in his meeting place, struck the poses requested by the photographer, and accepted the presence of the lights. Then he took me to Tarmadi, the right man, who listens little and speaks less. He is the custodian of a building where the Khaxsar dervishes meet, if I have understood correctly. Here lies the tomb of the great Sufi, Ali Ebne Sahl who died half a century ago.

But there is no dialogue with Tarmadi and soon you realize that it is not needed. Thin and lively at age sixty, he opens the gate, smiles at you between beard and moustache, and beneath those bushy eyebrows you discover the eyes of a child. He is dressed in dervish robes. He takes you into a room, sits down on the floor, and prepares tea. He does not speak. Tranquillity reigns.

One day I succeed in saying to him, through Simine.

"What is a Sufi?"

"Someone who has gone away."

Another day I asked him, "What is the road of the Sufi?"

He answered silently, tracing five words on the floor with his finger:

"I

You

I YOU

YOU"

"How can we travel this path?"

"With *Hu*."

"*Hu*?"

"Repeat it infinitely in your heart."

On the third day I asked him, "Can anyone become a dervish?"

He understood that I was speaking of myself.

"You can. You Christian?"

"Yes."

"No, then. Dervish is man of Islam."

I leave Persia, the country which gave us wheat. I have finished. I have met the Sufis, the photos are ready, the director is satisfied. There is always a wind blowing me somewhere.

You're a bit mad, really, a bit mad.

Dervish, man of Islam. That is why they were so elusive. "In one minute you may enter Islam," said Ruzbehan as we said goodbye.

No, I will not become a Sufi. I am a Christian and so I will remain. Not out of pride or faithfulness. In the Gospel there is a path, though it may be obscure, as Jesus said. It is obscure and has been obstructed. I will remain a Christian because one day, which I cannot remember, I was baptized in a tiny church in a village in the Prealpi. Perhaps these marks on the soul are indelible.

I prepare for more journeys: Siam, China, Japan, three Buddhist countries. I leave Islam where Allah is everywhere to go to the lands of Buddha, who erased God from his skies.

JOURNEY TO THE
FAR EAST

I am about to leave Bangkok and the Far East. At 5.30 tomorrow morning my flight leaves for India and I'll have to be at the airport an hour before departure. At 3.30 a.m. the taxi will come for me at the hotel, so there is no use trying to get any sleep. It's 11 p.m. I have just had dinner in my room. I have checked my ticket and my passport and packed my bag. Now I am relaxing in an armchair, jotting down these notes. Everything is ready. Everything is concluded, and I am expecting nothing, no one, or maybe I am waiting for someone to phone.

This is the same hotel room where I stayed last month, just back from Persia after my encounter with the dervishes. I was met at the airport by Enzo, an Italian building surveyor, a friend of my friends in Tehran who had informed him of my arrival. Enzo builds dams in Siam.

There is a chain of Italians working all across the globe. This network is similar to a series of radar installations. If you entrust yourself to one of them, you are passed on to the next whenever you move on to a new place. So you go from friendship to friendship, all of which have no basis except for the fact that you speak the same language: Italian.

Enzo introduces me to a princess.

"In Siam it is the princesses who open all doors."

The young women of Bangkok are charming, be they princesses or not. Petite, slender, and delicate. You see them on the streets in groups, like bouquets of flowers. They all have a spontaneous smile, a natural gaiety, a high, charming voice. Some possess perfect beauty, similar to goddesses to gaze at and admire, but not to touch – unreal, fleeting apparitions.

I have lunch at my hotel with Nala, a princess who possesses the enchantment of the East and the charm of Paris. She was educated in Lausanne. She is somewhere between Europe and Asia.

The vain male within me whom I had believed in hibernation reawakens during lunch and chases me out of the way. Throughout the meal, I witness my ability to be charming and amusing.

When lunch is over, she offers me a cigarette, but the dandy in me refuses, declaring somewhat allusively, "Since I have been in Asia, I have given up cigarettes, alcohol, and. . ."

Nala accepts the allusion and sips her coffee, observing me from below half-closed lids. She remarks, "In Europe sin is your speciality. You have even organized a hierarchy of sins: venial, capital, and original."

We finish our coffee.

"Thus you make sinners of newborn infants, terrify children, and send your dead to hell."

She lights her cigarette and says mockingly, "So, aren't you going to smoke with me?"

She has a lovely, concave face, and yet this fascinating creature soon caused me to flee all the way to Hong Kong.

The face of Master Ch'ang is terrible to behold. A

yellow face. He is a Taoist master in Hong Kong. He lives on a junk in the floating quarter of a city which is as beautiful as Rio de Janeiro, as clean as Rotterdam, as organized as Berne – and which has a skyline that rivals New York. The name "Hong Kong" means "Perfumed Lagoon". It is a magnificent place, perhaps even superior to Bangkok, perhaps superior to any other place on earth. If you visit it in a good season, you never want to leave. If you leave, you leave a part of yourself.

Ch'ang's face is terrible, though he is not. Fat belly, navel exposed, he is a master of Tao, which may be considered as a religion, a form of magic, a tradition, or a metaphysical system, depending on which expert you read. Except that the Taoists are either silent or declare (like the Sufis) that whatever can be named Tao is not Tao.

This may seem a hermetic statement but actually it is a technical one. The experience of Tao cannot be expressed in words, because it takes place on a level beyond the mind.

"It is technical, technical," shouts Ch'ang in a ringing voice, the only voice capable of silencing the din from the neighbouring boats.

It is a Chinese boat. I know nothing about boats, but this is a real Chinese boat, and more or less corresponds to our image of a Chinese sailing boat. A huge crowd of people are on board: infants crying, children playing, little boys diving into the water and then getting out and shaking themselves dry, sprinkling water all over you; chattering women, old women sewing, men eating very slowly, strangers passing by silently, people calling from the other boats. A young man naked, his body canary yellow, is defecating over the edge. In a corner of this chaos sits Master Ch'ang, squatting on his heels, fat, merry, and venerated. Around him, the smell of fish and of the sea.

His face is terrible at first sight. It doesn't even seem real, but rather a mask – Chinese to the extreme, round and wide; tiny slanting eyes, drooping moustache, his head shaved, like a character in a horror film. I am quite taken aback by it.

I had reached his boat after leaping across a series of other boats, barely managing to keep from falling into the sea, assisted by the hand of a stranger who had stopped me along the way, and had first offered to procure me a virgin, then opium, and at last, after understanding my tastes, had promised to find me a Taoist master at a cheap price. In Hong Kong you can find any kind of merchandise, and it always costs less than elsewhere.

After leading me to Master Ch'ang and receiving his tip, my native guide vanished. I found myself standing before that face and that belly, surrounded by all those Chinese. For a moment I felt quite intimidated and then I burst out laughing. Ch'ang joined in, and then everyone else laughed too, though they were ignorant of the reason which I alone knew. I was laughing at my own madness – imagining that my friend was there with me, the woman who says so sweetly, "You're a bit mad, really a bit mad."

If she had been there, who knows what she would have thought! Everyone was laughing. I was laughing harder than all the others because I was saying to myself as I looked at them: how will we communicate? They speak Chinese and I speak Italian. I am mad, really mad.

Yet we manage to communicate. Ch'ang (is that how you write it?) looks about fifty, my guide told me that he was seventy, and he claims to be ninety, but he's a real joker. We are able to speak to each other because he was a sailor in his youth and has sailed the seas, and speaks a few words of every language, including Genoese dialect.

His face is terrible, yet he is not. He is a strange combination of an old man and a child, more child than old man. He is always unpredictable, even when he cries out in a ringing voice, "Yes, it's technical, it's technical." He doesn't say this because he agrees with me, but because he never disagrees with anyone, as if there were some degree of truth in everything, a fact which is quite obvious to him.

Bangkok, Hong Kong, Bangkok, Tokyo, Bangkok, these are the stops in my journey to the Far East. Why three times in Bangkok? To see the bonzos, Maestra Poo, and the Buddha.

Do not chuckle, and do not judge me from below, don't say, "A charming concave face is what really drew you there."

We often find ourselves stalled along a road, unsure which way to turn until some hope appears, luring us on with its colours. After we have followed those colours and come to the journey's end, we sometimes realize that the real reason for our journey was something else entirely and that this path has taken us exactly where we wanted to go. Perhaps angels have no other way to help men.

However, after I met Nala, my Archangel began to fade.

Ch'ang's boat becomes my home throughout my stay in Hong Kong. I spent entire days there, and then returned quite late in the evening to the hotel, where the western guests were gathered round the television, worried about the fate of the first astronauts who had landed on the moon.

In alternating between the West on video and the East of the boat, I compared my entronauts to those astronauts. Once they had reached the moon, they showed us the earth: a tiny little ball lost in the indifference of the cosmos. On that tiny crust all mankind was gathered at that very moment, imperceptible, more insignificant than insects, perhaps more like mould. So infinitesimal that we needed help – men and women come here, let's not fight any more, we are nothing, let us gather together fragile and frightened and hold on to each other to keep ourselves warm. What good has our ingenuity done us in inventing the wheel and the motor if no one has been saved from death, not the first men or the last: all dead, all dying. We looked at the earth and then at the moon, dead, its craters empty. The astronauts have shown us our transitory nature.

The entronauts use a different language. Yes, we must leave the globe, ascend in the sky, we must defeat terrestrial gravity, the attraction of the ego which allows us to become individuals but which hinders our higher development. An inner cosmos awaits us, divine, immortal. The entronauts give us back our place at the centre of the universe.

This is what I said to myself as I went back and forth between the West on video and the East on the boat.

After a while, the boat people got to know me. I was the only white person who came to see them every day, leaping from boat to boat – those boats filled with ten thousand or one hundred thousand Chinese who were born, who lived and died a few inches from the sea. They all knew me, but I knew no one, rather I confused their faces and they all seemed alike to me just as our faces look alike to them. They might mistake a Sicilian for a Swede.

It was the children who got to know me best – as I handed around candy. They teased me by touching their noses – to indicate my European proboscis. Strangely enough, the very first day that they felt familiar enough to tease me, Ch'ang spoke to me about noses.

It was then that I had the first suspicion. I had just sat down on the floor next to him when he began to laugh and look at my nose, touching his own just like the children had done. How could he have known?

We spoke about noses and he asked me why mine was so big, and whether I knew how to use it.

"What should I do with it?"

"Breathe."

In those days I had begun to search for the Tao, locked in my room late at night with the lights out, not speaking to anyone.

After so many journeys and encounters, it seemed that I was beginning to understand. For example, the Leroys in Paris abandoned the prison of their senses and their mind. For the senses it was easy: in the dark with eyes closed, ears plugged, body relaxed. But the mind is a Van Allen belt and you cannot go beyond it. Or perhaps special fuel is needed. The mind belt stops you with its fascinating images: the lovely face of Nala smiling, the television of the hotel, the astronauts and the moon's crust. Hypnotized by these images, your consciousness drowns.

When you wake up you are in the same place, on the ground, a bit sleepy. So sleepy that you might as well go to bed. But before you go to bed, the verses of the ancient Sufi, Molana, come to mind, "Who is the intimate being who dwells in my eye and looks out?"

In those days I had secretly begun to search for the Tao and that was when I had the second suspicion. Ch'ang had asked me why I had such a big nose and if I knew how to use it.

"What should I do with it?"

"Seek Tao with your breathing."

A woman brought him a plate of fish and he began to eat it, now and then feeding me a bit with his own hands. The indigestion that has accompanied me throughout my life was delighted by those Chinese foods which it adored. But I was much more greedy to hear Ch'ang's explanation, though he was silent, "How does he know that I am looking for the Tao?" I began to suspect that this man was able to read my thoughts.

While he chewed he began looking at his big stomach, naked to the navel.

"Feel your breath."

He stopped eating and began to stare at his belly which moved up and down as he breathed, becoming calmer and calmer until at last it seemed completely immobile.

Ch'ang's eyelids were lowered and a strange smile had appeared on his lips. At that moment he no longer seemed fat or terrible, but he was different, and had become extraordinarily beautiful.

After a while he revived and repeated, "Feel your breath."

I thought to myself, "Breath is the fuel."

He agreed and said, "It is the fuel."

It was true, he could read my thoughts. I got up to leave and took a deep breath. Around me I could smell fish and the sea.

A telegram arrived from Nala, "Meeting arranged with Maestra Poo". So I rushed back to Bangkok for the second time, without asking my Archangel's opinion. At that time when the voice of Nala called, it silenced every other voice.

On the plane I found myself sitting next to a professor of sinology who had lived in the Far East for over thirty years. He knew everything about the Chinese.

"They think quite differently from us and the West cannot understand them. Do you know why Wei-yang, the great leader and victim of a murder plot, never managed to obtain supreme command? Because the conspirators were assassinated during his funeral. For us it is unthinkable than an event occurring after someone's death could have an influence on him during his lifetime. But for them, Wei-yang could never have become supreme leader because his funeral was marred by human victims. And do you know why the people of Beijing are very worried at the moment? Because certain birds have begun to destroy their own nests. They feel that the situation must be very grave if even birds have forgotten the bond of family love. You see the difference. We believe in cause and effect, but they follow the idea of meaningful correspondences. These are two ways of understanding the world, different but equally valid. If the world can be understood."

The professor indulged in his discoveries.

"Do you know who the real, age-old ruler of China is? The Tai Tai, or rather the first wife. After ten years of marriage, the Tai Tai begins to notice signs of distraction in her husband. So she says to him: 'My lord, you must remarry. I know a lovely young girl, who will do very well for you and for me, since I am no longer young.' The lovely young thing is a cousin of the Tai Tai who has planned it all and they have worked out the details together. The years pass and the Tai Tai commands her own children and those of the other wife. When the husband turns fifty, more signs of distraction are noted and so the first wife says, 'My lord, you must remarry. I know a young girl who would do very well for you, since I am getting old.' The husband is satisfied and the Tai Tai reigns supreme. The politics of China will remain obscure to those who do not take the Tai Tai into account."

While the sinologist was telling me about the third wife, I thought of Nala, the petite and charming princess with the tanned and concave face. I looked at the American air hostess, tall and robust, all breast and hips, more a mare than a woman.

I arrived in Bangkok for the second time.

Now in Bangkok for the third time, nestled in an armchair while I write these notes, I regret not having returned to Hong Kong and not having met Ch'ang again on his crowded boat smelling of fish and the sea.

It's midnight and in a few hours I will leave for India. Here everything is finished and I am not expecting anything or anyone, or perhaps only a telephone call.

I had spoken so often of Maestra Poo, and was impatient to meet her. Maestra Poo, an elderly woman, widow of an ambassador, a nun for many years, a very wise woman. I did not know that there were monasteries for women in Siam, rather I did not know that women of wisdom existed.

But as soon as I had abandoned Ch'ang and rushed back to Bangkok, I found that Nala had vanished. No one knew anything about her or about the telegram she had sent me. They told me that she had probably gone to Europe.

Her disappearance surprised me, then disappointed

me, and finally irritated me. Already prior to my departure for Hong Kong, my encounters with Nala had somehow gone wrong, without my understanding why. Every meeting ended in an argument, externally polite but actually quite harsh. I only had to say the word "bonzo" for example and she flew into a rage.

"That word has no meaning. No one here is called "bonzo", it's a depreciatory term you Europeans have invented."

Very pugnacious, but she does not raise her voice, she remains a princess. This is what irritated me. All the same I tried to smile and she answered me with her charming smile, but her melodious voice, designed for tenderness, grew shrill, "Yours are called priests, but ours are bonzos, yours are called saints, ours marabouts. And if we called St. Francis of Assisi a guru and the pope a bonzo? You are colonialists in everything. You claim to have a monopoly on God and aren't even ashamed."

I agreed but her irritation was contagious and made me the staunch defender of Christianity. I praised Thomas Merton, who died in Bangkok. She became even more beautiful when her eyes glinted with anger, because she wasn't angry with Christians but with me. To change the subject I began to talk about Maestra Poo, but this was a mistake.

"She lives a hundred kilometres from here on the sea. To persuade her to receive you I'll have to speak to her first. It won't be easy. Why don't you try one of the men's monasteries? There are nearly ten thousand of them."

No, I wanted Poo, a woman of wisdom. So Nala had said goodbye with a charming smile, and had offered me her hand to kiss.

All that hostility must have had some cause, if causes

exist and if the Chinese aren't right after all in believing that causes do not exist, only correspondences. But from our childhood we are conditioned to seek cause and effect in the world and we are unable to view things in any other way.

If it were just coincidence?

However, that vain male I carry in my belly had discovered the reason for Nala's irritation. He said, "The first day during lunch, you courted her, and then you stopped. That's why." Can a dandy see the truth? However, if this journey has meaning, it is not the search for caresses from Essy, Maggie or Nala, not the search for pleasure but for happiness.

Annoyed, I left for Hong Kong, leaving her a note. "Let me know when I may see Poo." After a month she wired me, but on my arrival she had disappeared and perhaps had gone to Europe.

Since Mistress Poo for the moment was not to be found, I began to seek out the bonzos, rather I mean the Buddhist monks. It's not too difficult; you can find them on the street. They wear saffron-coloured robes, the same colour as the overalls worn by road workers in our country. In Bangkok they are visible from a long way off.

All the Siamese become monks at least once in their lives, at least for a season or for a year or more. Buddha was a monk and from monkhood he passed to enlightenment. The imitation of Buddha is monastic. The imitation of Christ ought to take us into the desert for forty days after which we should move about from place to place. The idea makes us laugh and we would never allow our children to live without a fixed address. This shows that we are no longer Christians. Yet in Siam there are many Buddhists and they all wear saffron-coloured robes and shave their heads and beg for food, and then seclude themselves, chaste and silent, in a monastery. After this experience, they may decide to keep the robes or take a wife. The monk is a living ideal. People bow to them, offer them food and flowers. Everyone knows that these monks are journeying towards enlightenment while we toss about in our troubled dreams.

But in Bangkok a saffron robe does not make the monk. I realized this one day in the Chinese quarter when a young man with a faded robe crossed the street and stretched out his hand to me. This was scandalous because Buddhist monks never ask or say thanks. I offered him the roasted bananas I had bought for lunch, but he begged me gently, "Money please".

He took the money, lit a cigarette and began to walk beside me towards the temple of the Emerald Buddha. He had a drawn yet lovely face, a western face. His eyes were European in shape and colour, a bit wild. A half-blood? He spoke perfect English in a toneless voice, his words frequently interrupted by bouts of coughing. You might have thought he was English. Indeed he was.

I realized this from the way he looked at the girls. As we headed for the temple he said that he had been travelling for a couple of years. He hated the cold and in the East it was warm. He had no baggage and he wore this robe someone had given him, but he couldn't remember who and every now and then his parents sent him money from London. In the East you can live on nothing, even marijuana costs little. Yes, he had been smoking dope for the last three or four years; he had begun smoking at age seventeen and he couldn't live without it. He wouldn't live long, that he knew for sure.

"Isn't it nice and warm? There's the temple. That's

where I have been sleeping every night for the last month."

There was something very gentle and resigned about him. He was a vagabond, a hippy. If I had been thirty years younger I would have been one of them. They are on the side of the gardener, against the engineer. So am I. Try to teach them a lesson? He was too intelligent, had studied at Cambridge, and justified himself with a theory. I offered to accompany him to his embassy so that he could be repatriated, I offered to take him to see a doctor so that he could seek treatment.

But he just looked at me with a worried expression, "No, no, it's warm here and the people are fond of me."

It was true. They all knew him in the temple, he had been the guest of famous monasteries. They viewed his vice with indulgence. If he wants to live like that, why hinder him? Will he die soon? What is one lifetime if you consider that man is reborn innumerable times?

He had his own theory and he explained it to me a bit at a time with his toneless voice, though he frequently coughed and often lost the thread of what he wanted to say. It was a convincing theory.

"My father was a drug addict. How do I mean? Every evening after work he had to have his glass of whisky. Why? Because he needed to be physiologically happy. He had all the food and drink he needed, he got on well with my mother in every way, and he was healthy. So why did he need alcohol every evening? Look at that beautiful girl. I don't go with girls any more, I am no longer interested in them, but I still like to look at them. My mother takes drugs. What do I mean? As soon as she wakes up, she has to have a cup of coffee and then another after lunch, and at five she must have tea and after dinner another cup of coffee.

Why does she need caffeine every day? I will remain in the East until the end. With this robe, nobody asks me who I am and where I am going. My sister takes drugs. Cigarettes morning noon and night. 'Why does she need nicotine every day?' you might say to me, but if taken in small quantities it is not a drug. Yet it is. It is not a question of the amount or the effect, it's a question of the need. Men cannot be physiologically happy. London is frightening and cruel. Here people are kind and gentle. There is no population on the earth that does not use drugs in one way or another. Because we cannot live in normal consciousness. It is too narrow, arid, suffocating. We must expand it. That's why I take marijuana. Consciousness can be expanded with alcohol, caffeine, nicotine, cocaine, or opium; or with love, art, prayer, music, poetry, fasting, nature, rituals, God. And those who have none of these things at least sleep. In sleep and dream our consciousness expands. If you do not sleep, if you do not dream, you die. Your entronauts? Drugged with God. You want to see them? I'll take you. I know a monastery in the mountains. Siamese, Tibetan, Chinese. I lived there. Let's go, I'll take you."

We went. The monastery is located near the dam under construction and Enzo, the Italian building surveyor, loaded us onto a lorry along with sacks of cement. We left in the evening and night soon fell.

My companion fell asleep immediately. He could sleep anywhere in any position. I envied him, since I can only sleep on a mattress with a pillow. He slept, indifferent to the hard sacks, to the biting of the mosquitoes, and the rattling of the lorry. He coughed from time to time, poor boy, racked with consumption.

We arrived at dawn. The monastery was behind a forest, near the dam's construction site. When work on the dam is completed, it will all be submerged.

In the livid light of dawn the place looked different from what I had imagined. The golden light of the rising sun appeared and quickly spread across the horizon, colouring the sky with blue, the forest with green, illuminating the marshes and the saffron robes of the monks. The young Englishman headed towards them and soon disappeared in the midst without a word of goodbye to me, just as suddenly as he had appeared in the Chinese quarter of Bangkok. I didn't even know his name.

There was no monastery. Only an ancient pagoda and a tower, surrounded by very poor, cone-shaped huts. I looked at the pagoda, the huts and the monks from a distance and did not know what to do, awkward as usual in my shyness, overcome momentarily by my inability to speak the language and by a sense of futility. Ever since I had met Nala, my soul had closed and grown heavy, no longer in touch with the Archangel.

I was sleepy and hungry. I could hear the sound of the machines far away working on the dam. I went towards the dam site, leaving the pagoda behind me. I had a letter of introduction from Enzo for the Italian contractors who were directing the works. I introduced myself as a journalist and they greeted me, offering me food and lodging.

The word "journalist" is very powerful. It is an identity card, a passport, a certificate which justifies your peculiar behaviour and persuades others to help you.

I only had to mention that I had come to interview the head of the monastery and my appearance became plausible and soon everyone was working to help me. Every morning a few monks passed by the site to receive the offering of a few bowls of boiled rice.

Through them, I was told the next day that the head monk was expecting to meet the journalist who had come from Europe. I went immediately, armed with notebook and pen as if I had really come to interview him.

That happened after my return from Hong Kong and before my trip to Tokyo, during the time that Nala could not be found. It is the time that preceded my visit to Poo, ex-ambassadress, now Buddhist nun, and an innocuous old lady, you might say. And yet she terrified me so much that I grabbed my bag and took the first flight to India. There's always a wind blowing me somewhere.

Many things happened after my interview with the great bonzo, who was not great, but rather tiny, nor bonzo, (monk, says Nala). It was an authentic interview with questions, answers, and rapid considerations that I jotted down on the spot. Now re-reading it for the first time, I discover the limitations of interviews, of their pretext of information, of their hurried and skeletal superficiality, and yet in this one there is enough to shatter our convictions.

I see myself in the shadow of the pagoda, next to the great monk in his ochre robe, his head shaved, his face wizened but calm and gentle, willing to satisfy my curiosity, willing to try to understand me. Explaining is the first duty of the ascetic.

He was sitting cross-legged on the ground, in the same position as the golden Buddha looming behind him. I sat on the ground facing him, in that position which was so easy for him, and so unbearable for me, which made my ankles and joints ache.

This is what I wrote while the monk smiled at me and the Buddha smiled at me from above.

"A day in the life of a monk?"

"At dawn he wakes. When the sun is up, a walk. Always in the open air. Once a day he allows one of the faithful to fill his bowl with rice or vegetables."

"How big is his bowl?"

"The size of a hand."

"Meat?"

"Never. Compassion for all living creatures."

"Money?"

"Never. He may accept only vegetable foods. He drinks water from the fountains."

"How often does he eat during the day?"

"Once, between nine and ten."

"And if no one gives him anything?"

"He fasts."

"What does he do all day?"

"He walks, concentrating on his inner life, the goal of reawakening, the model the Buddha has given us."

"And if people ask him questions?"

"He offers instruction, advice, and assistance to all impartially, all men being equal, that is all creatures, animal and vegetable united in compassion, everyone must be helped, even a grain of dust."

"Women?"

"The ascetic is chaste and is respected by women."

"Poverty and chastity, are those his perpetual vows?"

"Perpetual vows? He is poor and chaste not because of some obligation, but of his free choice. He has chosen freedom and he continues to choose it. It is clear to him that there is no freedom in money but only pain, no freedom in women but only tribulation."

"And if he should get tired of this life?"

"He leaves his robe and does what he likes."

"And if he should regret it?"

"He takes back his robe."

"His vows of obedience?"

"Obedience? To whom?"

"And at night?"

"He returns to the place where he sleeps, away from inhabited areas: in a monastery, pagoda, or cave, under a tree. He sleeps sitting up, with his back resting against some support. If he lies down it is in the position of the Buddha, on his right side."

"Bed?"

"We do not know the meaning of that word."

"Doesn't the monk complain about such a hard life?"

"A hard life? Why hard (he looks at me surprised, silent, and makes an effort to understand me and then to make me understand)? No, it is not hard, but envied. The ascetic is a free man, his time and destiny are his own. Everyone desires this freedom."

"And material well-being?"

"What do you mean?" (He sincerely doesn't understand.)

"The high standard of living in Bangkok."

"Bangkok. Have you seen how many poor people there are?" (Twenty years ago there were five hundred automobiles in Bangkok, now there are five hundred thousand, and the poor Siamese must make an effort to maintain them and to earn their living, so much toil, so many aspirations, desperation, bank loans, work, work, work and it's never enough. Exhaustion, envy, rivalry, disappointment, misunderstandings, solitude, fleeting pleasures: you run, you fail, your desires multiply, you suffer from an itch that never goes away, you scratch until you bleed and then you die.)

"For you, people who drive automobiles are poor?"

"Poor people without peace, without joy in a troubled dream."

It is the hour of sunset, the privileged hour of inner

life. If God is being and goodness, material well-being is nothing. The great monk withdraws, leaving me with a quotation.

"The wandering ascetic drifts about without a home, without money, his head shaved, his soul serene."

Then he bows. "You may come back tomorrow."

He leaves, tiny and wise.

I return the next day. Along the way I think of Nala's protests. "If Buddhist monks set fire to themselves in Bangkok, you call them fanatics. If a student in Prague imitates him, you call him a martyr."

First question: "The ascetic walks along concentrating on his inner life. That means . . . ?"

"His conscious life."

"Explain."

"Close your eyes. Can you feel where your consciousness is located?"

"I don't know. Perhaps behind my forehead."

"You must invigorate your consciousness and never lose track of it. Inhabit it."

"How?"

"Put it in your breath. Move it around. Put it in your feet and it will free you from thoughts. Put it in your heart and it will bring inexplicable joy. Put it above your head and it will enlighten you in immensity (yes, the word is indeed *to enlighten*, and *immensity*, as in Ungaretti's poem. Here in this pagoda in the middle of nowhere, I reconfirm the greatness of poets). Once consciousness has been found, you become aware of the forces within you which move you and rather than being controlled by them, you learn to control them. You penetrate the inner world, the path to immortality. But you need a master."

"How does one become a monk? Are there rituals, dogmas, sacraments for this purpose?"

"No, the Buddhist is someone who seeks refuge in Buddha. He declares: 'I seek refuge in Buddha, in law and in the Order.' Over the centuries there have been differences in certain aspects of monkhood in different Buddhist countries, but the form does not change. In order to seek refuge, we must feel afraid."

"What do you mean?"

"You must see the world as Buddha saw it."

"Explain."

He was silent.

As I think back on this journey to the Far East, not everything is clear to me. Bangkok becomes confused with Hong Kong and Tokyo. It's very late, I'm tired, my notes are all a muddle.

Nala, Ch'ang, the English boy, the great bonzo, Nala, Enzo, Uyeshiba, Nala, Poo. Something is missing: the Archangel. The only thing clear to me is that I'll soon be on my way to India.

I arrived in the middle of the night in Tokyo, escorted by Typhoon Gloria. Meteorologists always give women's names to typhoons. I had left the spring behind in Bangkok but it had given me no delight because I was in a bad mood.

Bad moods are the tumefaction of the soul. An angry tumefaction which demands an outlet, which we find in taking it out on people or circumstances which have nothing to do with our problem and which in other conditions wouldn't have bothered us, but which now irritate us. The delayed flight, a clerk's error, nearly tripping on the steps, all give me a chance to express my anger. This need to let off steam makes us forget the real reason, the blow received some time ago.

While flying towards Tokyo I tried to think back and

discover who had given me this blow. It certainly was not the great bonzo who had offered me advice for my inner life, nor the young Englishman poisoned by marijuana who vanished without telling me his name. The tumefaction which had created my bad mood was due to another disappearance: Nala.

As I thought about her, her beauty faded. Her face reminded me of the face of a Pekinese, one of those cute little dogs who welcomes you with a wagging tail, rubs against your legs and abruptly falls in love with you, and then for no reason suddenly turns hostile and begins to bark and if you reach out to pet her she tries to bite your hand or runs away. You want to call her, look for her, but you have no idea where to look.

What sort of thing is that to do, to send a telegram and then to disappear?

I arrived in the night with Gloria, and when the hatch of the plane was opened I went out into the freezing rain. "Damn it, it's raining," I cursed, unaware that we were surrounded by a typhoon which had swept away villages and whole sections of the coast, unaware that the plane had barely managed to land. I knew nothing about Typhoon Gloria, and nothing about typhoons. I behaved as if I had just got off the train from Milan to Lucerne and had found a thunderstorm.

I walked down the ramp, annoyed. "What rotten weather." The typhoon took my breath away, whipped the umbrella out of my hand, poured water down into my face so that I could not see, and in a few minutes I was as wet as if I had fallen into a quagmire. I was indignant. "Just look at how much it rains in this country." Lafcadio, Lafcadio.

I dragged my bad mood to the passport control desk (they were very meticulous), to the customs control (even more meticulous) and to the airline ticket counter (inept). The Japanese clerk said, "I am very sorry but we have been unable to find you a hotel room."

"What? In Bangkok they assured me that . . . "

"I am very sorry."

It was one o'clock in the morning, local time. Lafcadio, Lafcadio, where is your Japan?

"You have come to Tokyo to see Master Uyeshiba?" She pronounced these words as though she were saying, "Just look how stupid some people can be."

I was speaking to a lady in the diplomatic circle, who completely lacked diplomacy.

Luca reproaches her. "What do you know about it?"

We are having lunch in a restaurant in Ginza. Luca is my host and I must play the guest of honour, in a party of five or six Italians, men and women. We are eating raw fish, rice, unfamiliar vegetables, fruit I have never seen before, sipping thin broths, and mysterious essences, all in little plates and cups in which the food and drink are arranged like flowers in a flower garden.

"Master Uyeshiba is ninety years old. Nobody sees him, they treat him like a god."

Luca repeats, "What do you know about it?"

"I know everything about *aikido*. He refuses to see anyone. I did not manage to see him."

Her failure requires me to fail as well, otherwise she will be offended.

Luca saved me. In the chain of Italian radar, he is the Tokyo connection. Enzo relayed the news of my arrival to him from Bangkok. Luca swept me away from the airport, found me a hotel room, and offered me consolation in this city which had rejected me from the outset, greeting me with freezing rain, overcrowding, ugly women, squalid streets with no names so that there are no taxis to take you where you want to go. Lafcadio, Lafcadio, where is your Japan?

This woman joins the club.

"But you've come all the way from Rome to Tokyo just to see Uyeshiba?"

Luca intervenes. "Don't listen to her. I'll find you an interpreter and everything will be easy. Who is this Uyeshiba?"

Another guest answers, "He's a doctor, quite famous. He was in Italy for awhile. Yes, a doctor."

"That's not true," says the woman and an argument ensues.

After a pause the young girl who up to now has done nothing but powder her nose suddenly pipes up, "Isn't he that singer?"

Lafcadio, Lafcadio.

The story of Uyeshiba would have pleased Lafcadio Hearn, who was born on a Greek island, grew up in England, became an American journalist and spent many years in Japan, an experience from which he drew the inspiration for his charming books. He loved this land so much that he became a Japanese citizen, took the name Koizumi and died in Tokyo in 1904. At that time, Uyeshiba was twenty-one years old. Perhaps they met.

Master Uyeshiba was born in one of the villages which Lafcadio describes, in an archaic Japan in which young girls were called *Ine*, which means "rice shoots". From his youth, he was obsessed with the idea of *budo*, a word which cannot be translated because it eludes meaning.

(Approximate definition of *budo*: ancient martial

discipline which teaches one how to fight not in order to overcome an adversary but to change oneself. Another definition: a fighting technique which substitutes invincible, inner energy for muscular strength. Last definition: the art of fighting and of the bow which as a spiritual path may take man to what he is already but does not realize he is. The Japanese say all this in the word *budo*.)

So from his early youth, Uyeshiba began to think constantly about *budo*. At age seven he was educated by a Buddhist monk, and at ten, by a Zen master. At fourteen he witnessed a few bullies from his village mistreat his beloved father. He suffered so much at the sight of this that he vowed to himself that he would become such a strong man that no one would ever dare do such a thing to his father again. So *budo* became even more an obsession for him. He visited the places where the masters of the arts derived from ancient *budo* (*udo, kendo, sumo, kyudo*) lived. He learned these arts and excelled in them and thus became famous. However, he remained restless, searching for a spiritual truth to dedicate himself to, a truth that cannot be formulated nor defined, a truth to live.

His father grew ill and the doctors despaired. The son rushed to Ayabe, where the venerable Deguchi, the head of the esoteric school Omotokio lived, in the hopes that his father could be healed through spiritual means. Instead, his father died.

His pain was very great. This death increased his need for the truth. He often left his village and went to the mountains and spent his time meditating among the rocks. In 1919 he moved to Ayabe with his family. He lived in a solitary house, carrying on his research.

At the age of forty-two, in the summer of 1925 he was enlightened. He has tried to describe this experience. It was an exemplary illumination, descended from a high heaven, because there are higher and lower heavens. Words however are inadequate to describe it, yet master Uyeshiba made an attempt to do so, more or less as follows:

One spring day he was walking alone in his garden. Suddenly his soul burst open (as though ripped open by a bolt of lightning) and the universe appeared transfigured to his eyes, full of light, pervaded by the divine spirit, presence, love, joy in every being and everywhere. It seemed to him that it was in us and yet we do not see it.

Then abruptly (how much time had passed?) he found himself in his garden, in a state of astonishment, his face bathed in tears. This undeniable sacred encounter changed his existence.

Thus was born the martial discipline of *aikido*, daughter of the ancient *budo*.

(Westerners who consider numbers important will be impressed by these: 300,000 disciples of *aikido* in Japan, 100,000 abroad, all devoted to Master Uyeshiba.)

I saw him. Despite the all-knowing lady, I saw him and talked to him.

In reality things looked quite bleak. The Japanese interpreter whom Luca procured turned out to be a middle-aged woman: ugly, badly dressed, inhibited, too shy to look you in the eyes, to speak to you without covering her mouth with her hand, or to smile without turning her face in the other direction. These coy adolescent manners in such a withered old maid would have annoyed even Lafcadio. We were in a taxi, heading towards the *aikido* centre, but the driver had taken the wrong road. In Tokyo the streets have no names, and addresses are always approximate. So to my annoyance with the old maid were added the endless ticking of the meter and the miserable rain. I was very irritated. Naturally, the great old man was not to be found at the centre.

His son was there – of little interest to me. He offered me tea. "The master appears rarely, sometimes at four in the morning. He is eighty-six years old. Exercises are done on the first floor." He showed me a book and I bought it. The interpreter did not understand very well and translated even worse. I hardly listened to her. This trip to Tokyo had been a waste of time. Tomorrow I would leave. India is the land of seekers. What do I care about *Budo aikido*?

Suddenly there was a great bustling around the entrance. The interpreter said, "The master, unexpectedly."

He was wearing a traditional robe. He walked straight towards me and looked at me kindly. I was standing respectfully against the wall in the corridor. He looked at me. Large, luminous, blue eyes. Blue eyes? Impossible.

He disappeared through a door. The interpreter suggested, "Shall we go up to the first floor?"

We went up to a large room where fifty young men and a few teachers dressed in traditional *judo* attire were absorbed in martial exercises. I crouch in the corner and observe. A sudden murmur: the master has appeared in the doorway.

With a rapid step he enters the room and comes towards me. I get up, embarrassed, and try to smile. We are standing face to face. His face looks twenty years younger than his ninety years. The only signs of his age are the large freckled spots on his skin. Now his eyes are black. He bows three times. I would like to reply, to thank him, yet I do nothing, I just stand there like an idiot, and blush in front of everyone.

He speaks in Japanese. The interpreter translates now and then, and yet I understand because he illustrates his words with examples. He calls one of his disciples (among the fifty silent men kneeling by the wall) and invites him to join him on his platform. He gives an order and the disciple throws himself at him with all his might, following the rules of *aikido*, but the master blocks him with a finger (yes, a ninety-year-old finger) blocks him and sends him spinning across the room. It is incredible, but true.

This miracle is repeated three, six, ten times. The old man makes a minimum of movements – florid gestures which involve no use of his muscles, and yet those young men are dashed to one side like paper in the wind.

Then he calls a very tiny man and asks him to concentrate on his *hara*, a secret point below the navel, the inner centre of gravity, the source of power. The disciple closes his eyes for a long moment, then opens them and gives a sign to indicate that he is ready. He reaches out his arm. Three, then five men cling to it, and yet it does not bend, it has turned to steel.

Another slim man roots himself in the ground and four men are unable to move him, for his body has become lead.

Finally the old man has his adversaries arm themselves with huge sticks while he wields only a pencil. The blows do not reach him. The pencil gently blocks each blow from the attackers, who, when touched by an electric charge (invisible, incredible, yet evident) are hurled across the room. What power does this man have and how does he transmit it to his disciples?

He has finished. He looks at me. His big luminous

eyes are now blue again. He bows and goes out, leaving me with an essential truth: physical strength comes from the inner man.

I go out. It is no longer raining. Suddenly Tokyo is shining in the sun.

Then I rushed off to Bangkok for the third time after receiving another message from Nala (*Appointment with Poo arranged*). The same words which had first sent me running from Hong Kong now compelled me to rush away from Tokyo.

In Bangkok, Nala is waiting for me at the airport. She is standing behind the barriers, beyond the passport and customs control. I can see her in the distance and raise my arm to wave at her, delighted to see her again. Our arguments, her disappearance, and the bitterness all forgotten.

As I go through the various check points I begin to consider my journey and my destiny. We do not have one destiny but many ascending destinies. My body was born with a destiny: perhaps its destiny is a long life. But it has been imprisoned by my heart which is easily exalted or depressed. It is the heart which may make the body ill, the heart which has its own fate that originates in its impulses, my heart has shortened the life of my body. Both of these are guided by the mind which has encountered certain ideas and has tried to put them into practice, thus transforming the destiny of heart and body. Then above all of these is the spirit, which in me is obscured by thoughts and impulses but which in others is luminous, capable of undermining established destinies and pointing the way to a new one.

As I rushed back to Bangkok I surrendered to the movements of my heart. My body follows, my mind observes, my spirit is silent – the Archangel.

Lovely Nala close up, a bit thin, veiled in melancholy.

"Where have you been?"

"I have been at Poo's convent. I couldn't bring myself to leave."

"Why were you so angry with me?"

"It annoyed me to think that you had come from Europe to search for our wisdom, while I was in search of your folly."

"And now?"

"Tomorrow Poo is expecting us."

We walked towards the exit, holding hands in the crowd.

That all happened last week. Then we went to the women's monastery. Not much happened there. An old woman took off her clothes. Not much, almost nothing. Yet I am unable to put these notes in order. It's three o'clock in the morning, these are my last few hours in Bangkok, before my departure for India. No one has rung and no one will ring. An old woman took off her clothes.

Poo, a toothless nun, widow of an ambassador, seventy or eighty years old, an old, bent body in a white tunic, a trembling voice, trembling hands. The little houses of her monastery are built at the foot of the hills near the sea.

"Maestra, a great bonzo told me that in order to understand I must see the world as Buddha saw it. How did he see it?"

Her eyes are dulled by age.

"Empty."

Young eyes of Nala on the beach, the long line of her back exposed down to the dimples of kidneys.

"Why empty? The world is full of things. Nature is horrified by the void. Look around. The world is full. Maestra, here we are in front of your house, a cart passes by."

"There is no cart. Remove the wheels and the axles and it is undone. Pieces, not a cart. The cart is only in your head."

"In my head? In that case I am the inventor of the wheel. . ."

"There is no wheel. Remove the circle and the spokes, it is undone. Pieces not a wheel. The wheel is only in your mind."

Remove the pieces and it is undone. I thought about it all day long. Then I said to myself, this old woman must be crazy. And the house where she lives, where she sleeps?

"There is no house. Remove the roof, the walls, can't you see it is undone? Pieces. The house is only in your mind.

Nala laughs, in a good mood today, while we walk amid the hills, in all shades of green.

Remove the pieces, can't you see it is undone? I thought about it all day long. Then I said to myself, this old woman is crazy, but I wasn't so sure any longer.

"Maestra, must I see everything as empty?"

"Even when you look at the castle in the clouds, it is already becoming undone. Even you, when you remember things that happened ten years ago: people, places, things. Where are they? Undone, in ten years, today."

Take away the pieces, can't you see that it is all undone? I thought about this for another day. Ten years, the pieces are gone and everything is undone. Then I said, she is a crazy old woman. If you take the pieces away then where do you end up?

"Then Maestra, what are we?"

"Bubbles in a stream, empty."

Nala stretched out on the beach, sleeping. She is not empty, it is true. I leave her sleeping and go back to Poo.

"Maestra, Nala is not empty."

She stares at me with her dull eyes. Then silently her trembling hands slowly open her white tunic. She is naked underneath: flaccid skin, sagging breasts and belly, blistered thighs, varicose calves.

She smiles toothlessly and yet tenderly at my horror, having offered herself beyond shame as an example.

"Poo is undone. Nala will be undone."

I run away. I rush back to the beach horrified. Nala comes towards me smiling. I see the teeth fall out of her mouth one by one. Flaccid skin invades her breast, and her legs are covered by varicose veins. Horror spreads across her youthful body.

"Don't you feel well?"

"Nala, I must go."

As I left her, "If you come back to Bangkok, please telephone me."

"Yes, of course, if I come back."

It is 3.30 in the morning. The taxi is ready. No one has rung.

These notes from the Far East are obscure, obscure as my own soul. Buddha did not want me, just as Allah did not want me.

Immense India is waiting for me. There is always a wind blowing me somewhere. Where will I go? Suddenly a voice whispers in my ear (the Archangel): Benares.

SECOND JOURNEY
TO INDIA

If an Indian wants to sell you something, don't refuse it. Buy it immediately. In the hotel in New Delhi an Indian with a charming smile tried to sell me a Japanese film camera. I told him that I had just come from Japan, but that did not discourage him. Then I told him that I didn't know how to use a film camera, but that didn't discourage him either. He smilingly went on listing the positive features of film cameras for me.

I turned away, but found him again at the Tibetan market where he gave me some excellent advice about what to buy there before going into a demonstration on how to use the camera. I walked away, but found him again at the travel agency where he managed to get me booked on a flight to Benares, quite a difficult feat. Then he launched into his speech again praising the advantages of owning a film camera. He promised that he would let me have it on a trial basis – first he would teach me how to use it, and if I was not satisfied I could give it back. No strings attached, except that I was to purchase the film for it exclusively from him. He smiled and convinced me. Now I know how the Indians managed to take control of all commerce along the coast of Africa as far as the Canary Islands. Such insistence finally coaxed a smile from my Archangel.

I accepted the trial period and he became my tour guide. Twenty emperors are buried in New Delhi and I filmed the tombs of every one of them. Seven cities were built upon that spot over the course of nine hundred years, and I filmed them all, along with the Red Fort, the Gateway to India, and Gandhi's funeral urn.

A few days later, the smiling Indian had sold me the camera, the accessories, and a huge quantity of film and had infected me with the cinema bug. When it was time for me to leave for Benares, he accompanied me to the plane. As I said goodbye to him I was convinced that he had taken advantage of my ingenuous nature.

But rather his help was invaluable. I owe it to him if I now possess a vivid, moving, colourful testimony of my travels in India. It's all here in these forty-one colour films which are poorly numbered and incomprehensible to everyone except myself.

I select them now at random and project them onto a small screen and dictate into the machine the story of my long pilgrimage across the continent of the entronauts.

Film 1. Benares: the airport, afternoon. Packs of striped, mongrel dogs greedy for any form of food cluster around the plane – skeletal, mangy, trembling. I think of my plump, cheerful and beloved bulldog. Injustice among dogs.

Close up of a dog's face. An intelligent, questioning look in his eyes. Human eyes. No, an inaccurate comparison. When have I ever seen such expressive eyes in a human being?

Groups of green, yellow, and red rickshaws gathered around the passengers. The coolie's son has become a cyclist. They are thin and dressed in rags. I think of our rough and ready porters with their bellies full of food and drink. Injustice among men. Why such injustice? The Archangel is silent.

There he is in the middle of the crowd of rickshaw drivers: Rao. He's the shy one standing at the back. Now he is giving up and going away. Rao became my regular driver.

All the passengers choose the bus to take them to the hotel.

And the Ganges? Where is the Ganges?

Film 5. Benares: dawn. In a boat on the Ganges, twenty metres from the bank. The boatman is talking to me, his words are incomprehensible. I nod. The camera is pointed east, waiting for the sun to rise. The horizon is bluish, then pale, then amber. Then the rosy aurora of India appears. There it is: the impetuous herald rising from the desert. (In a couple of minutes we will meet Kapila, the Tantric master I met here on this very same day.) On one bank, the desert, on the other: Babel, and in the middle the great noble Ganges, flowing slow, yellow-green in colour. This is Benares.

On the south side lies the desert: sand, dunes, gravel. Not a tree or a blade of grass, or a street or a house or an inhabitant, not even a solitary passer-by. Only a few vultures on the ground, immobile, sinister, waiting for the river to bring them some carrion. Silence, emptiness, solitude. It is the dead, cursed bank. The moon.

On the north bank, Babel. Sloops, fishingboats, small ships. Long stairways and ramps leading high up to temples, colonnades, verandas. People everywhere, in every pose, dogs, monkeys, doves, lamps, fires, smoke, drums, bells, and choruses. This is the living bank, it is blessed, it is man.

"Why is it that only this side of the bank is sacred?"

Sacred. What does that word mean? To us, nothing. For us the commercial value of land is sacred. We would never have left a bank of the Tiber, the Seine, the Thames, or the Hudson undeveloped. How can we understand the Indians? Perhaps they have access to a dimension where one place is sacred and another is profane. Before Romulus founded Rome, he determined its sacred spot. We went on building it on a plain of dangerous quicksand.

At my signal, the boatman rows me back towards the bank. The camera focuses on the people along the bank at sunrise. In India man is not limited by western measures. He lives for other hopes (yes, yes, soon we'll see Kapila.).

Film 6. Benares, morning, on a boat on the Ganges, along the bank: people immerse themselves in the water. The men, naked except for their loin cloths, go in up to their heads. The women, wrapped in muslin which clings modestly to their bodies when drenched, go in as far as their hips. The people immerse themselves in the water and remain there, their lips vibrating in arcane syllables, their hands raised in ritual gestures.

Their expressions intent, absent or radiant. They go into the water, stand a while, then return to the bank. Sculptured figures, clean, shining, living dark bronzes, pale antique marbles, the sweet sinuousness of the young girls, the proud nakedness of the youths. The simplicity of the eternal form of man. Even the Archangel has a man's shape, with wings.

The camera moves across a panorama of heads, feet, shoulders, and knees in motion, goes up a stairway, encounters a solitary ascetic sitting immobile, wrapped in a piece of ochre cloth, facing the sunrise. Only his head, his long, flowing black hair and beard emerge from the cloth. It is Kapila.

Film 12. Benares noon. Under a tree: this is Kapila's group. (Before this one there are five other films, but I can't find them. They must be mixed up with the others, or perhaps I lost them during the trip.) It is the group of Kapila's followers. Many of their faces are unfamiliar to me. People were always changing. Some left, others joined. There were only a couple of faithful disciples. For example, Freddy, the American, the one with the red hair, naked except for his loincloth. He is the one with the freckles and the scar on his chest, like some ancient warrior. He is speaking to another faithful disciple, the dark-skinned Raman, from Bengal, who has another name, but everyone called him Raman. As for me, they dubbed me with the nickname, "Italian", and never referred to me by any other name. How could I tell them about the three Swiss races?

Here is Kapila's head. He has the light skin of a European and the noble features of certain Arab faces. The camera catches him in profile, but you can't see him very well. Only when you look directly into his eyes do you understand who he is. Everything happened because those eyes looked at me.

Film 10. (This is one of the earlier ones. I find it in a corner, along with numbers 7 and 11.) Benares, day. Riding about on Rao's tricycle. The many styles of India: all the marvels of the East: Arab arcades, Persian minarets, Egyptian pyramids, Chinese pagodas. Algerian casbahs, Venetian Calle, the Albaicin of Granada. I leave the present and discover Rome in the early Middle Ages, with its throngs of pilgrims, the multiracial crowds of Carthage, the bizarre clothing of the Babylonian multitudes. Where am I? In what moment of time?

A force seems to weigh down upon Benares, which slowly invades you. You can feel it vibrating all around you. It penetrates your head and belly, filling you with a sense of restlessness. Archangel, Archangel, where are you leading me? Perhaps from a Mediterranean civilization towards a planetary one.

I visit a million altars, among colourful and gesticulating gods. Red Ganesh the pachyderm. Yellow Hanuman the anthropoid. Purple Vishnu omnipotent. The black lingam, generator of life. White-eyed Kali, the devourer. Blue Krishna, musician. The faces of the gods are as many and as varied as the souls of men.

Rao is twenty years old, thin and poor. He pedals all day long, sweating beneath the tropical sun and yet he enjoys a chat and gives me metaphysical replies.

"Rao, are the gods real?"

"Of course."

"As real as we are?"

"Oh, much more real than we are."

Perhaps he is right. What is real about us? We are so fragile, ephemeral, and fleeting. We accuse them of polytheism and are ready to condemn them for it. Rather it means that divine mercy is available to all, in a form that each one of us may understand and imagine.

"To the Ganges, Rao, let's go back to the Ganges. I want to see that ascetic again, the one we saw the other morning wrapped in the yellow cloth."

Rao knows everything about Benares. "That is Kapila, the Tantric master."

Tantra? Rao pronounces this word with reverent awe. The practitioners of Tantra are ascetics who have learned to master the forces unleashed during the act of physical union. Thus they are chaste. Tantra? Rao's awe intrigues me deeply.

But before that, I went to see the funeral pyres. Here's the film.

Film 7. Benares, sunset. The funeral pyres. You reach the pyres following the cadavers, quite different from our own dead. There are no grave diggers, no oppressive coffins. Look at them, all wrapped up in pink muslin and fastened with a string here and there. This is enough to simplify the human form and efface its individuality. Two bamboo poles are the stretcher. Two relatives in front and two behind can easily carry it on their shoulders. A few friends present. They are speaking calmly. There are no women about, not even at the pyres. They might weep and tears are unsuited to this ritual.

Twilight. There on the river you can see the flames. They never go out, they burn all day and all night. They have never been extinguished in ten thousand, or in twenty thousand years. Those fires were already burning when Buddha came to Benares. Buddha, the heretic rejected by India, just as Luther was rejected by the Latin world.

Close-up of a pyre, the wood stacked tidily. Small low-leaping flames. It doesn't take much to devour a human shape. All around the black-skinned attendants skilfully perform their task amid those flames flickering in the thick smoke nourished by our own substance. The flames quickly transform the body into steam and ashes and render it so volatile that the very image of death vanishes. All that is left are burning coals among the coals. A few blue flames flicker out. It is over. The ashes are dumped in the Ganges.

Another corpse arrives, the relatives gather round,

calmly observing. The young widower has the task of igniting the first piece of wood. Why isn't this man weeping for the bride he has lost? For me death is final. For him it is a transition. He himself is dead to all his past existences.

Film 11. Benares. Morning in the hotel, and then the Ganges. The hotel: old, comfortable, colonial. Morning tea, breakfast, lunch, afternoon tea, dinner. A profusion of servants in dress uniforms. I focus the camera on the face of an American tourist.

"Those pyres are disgusting. They have no respect for the dead. We make the dead beautiful, mould their lips into a smile, urge them to rest, place them in an expensive coffin, transport them to panoramic places, seal them in atomic bomb-proof tombs with music piped in where they may rest undisturbed for five hundred years."

"*Illusio perpetua amen.*"

"What? You are an European, aren't you? What about respect for life. Don't you see that human life is precious?"

Perhaps in New York, but not in Benares. The human life covering the earth has produced billions of examples over the course of the millennia. Not one has ever been saved, all have been reduced to ashes. When you proclaim: "Human life is precious," you are really thinking only about your own hide. Enough of that hypocrisy. Human life is not precious. Everyone knows that it has no value at all.

I ask Rao to stop so that we may film a group of sick people who are being taken to the Ganges in hopes of dying in that privileged place. Then a long row of old men who have come here to wait for the end. For an Indian there is no better fate than to die in Benares.

Superstition – says the American – in order not to undermine his mental catalogue.

Rao, is it superstition or a vibration?

He does not answer me and has not understood. Perhaps everything is vibration. In bodies, heat, sound and light are vibrations. In the mind thoughts oscillate, and in the spirit, the blessed rhythms of the empyrean and the beating of the Archangel's wings. Perhaps everything vibrates, perhaps the high tension of Benares is transmitted to the soul, guaranteeing a good death and perhaps even more? If this were so, then superstition becomes wisdom in a vibrating universe.

These are the last sequences of film 11. There down by the bank sits Kapila in the shadow of a wall, surrounded by five or six people. The film ends, but my memory begins just at that point.

I approach cautiously without being too obvious, urged on by my hopes, blocked by my feelings of awe. My hope is to understand death, like any Indian widower. I am awed by the word "Tantra" which evokes occult powers.

Kapila is speaking to one or two people in his group in English, a language which I cannot bear; I detest it so much that I consider my ignorance of it as something noble. Why didn't the Romans conquer Asia? In that case, Tantric texts would have been written in Latin and Latin would have been the language spoken by Kapila.

Crazy ideas, born from my fatigue. I suddenly feel that I can't go on any more. Exhausted after so many airplanes, so much indigestible food and drink, so many beds and so many languages, but most of all I am tired of myself, tired of dragging myself around all day long and going to bed at night, tired of hearing myself think with never an end to it, always the same old thoughts.

Tired of witnessing the perpetual changing of my moods: now satisfied now irritated by the tiniest things, by good or bad weather, by the silence or words of others, by my nostalgia or my hopes. Constant variations – expansion at the smallest pleasure, contraction at the most mediocre discontent. Enough. And finally tired of a search that has led me nowhere, that has changed the sky over my head, but not my inner world, tired of a search which has shown me the greatness of others, leaving me the unchanged spectator. I can no longer bear it.

I lean my back against the wall and try to cross my legs, but I find this position impossible for it makes all my joints ache. I let myself go and lie down on the ground like a beggar. At that moment Kapila notices me.

Kapila, who is sitting a few feet away, looks over at me. A noble Arab face, large, luminous eyes. The expression in them is exceptionally gentle and penetrates my bitterness. A penetrating yet fraternal glance. A burden is lifted from my heart and a feeling of tranquillity floods through me, a breath of relief is kindled in me, along with an indifference towards myself. What miracle is this? Archangel, Archangel, is this your gift?

I do not move. Kapila gets up and goes away with the others, after pausing for a long moment to gaze at me. Should I speak? No, finally I am silent.

Film 15, dedicated to Freddy. Freddy, the red-haired American, medium weight, freckled, long red hair, beard. He dives into the Ganges as if he were on Long Island, dispensing with ritual gestures. He swims out in long gleeful strokes. Freddy is the typical American at age thirty – in his speech, gestures, manner of laughing, and even the pipe he smokes. He could be a sailor. You wonder how he ended up in India and became one of Kapila's disciples. Then with a word, a gesture, or a decision, you discover that he has a deep, delicate flowing soul.

Here is another scene. Freddy, trying to hand around bowls of food, but encountering great difficulty. Indians, so famous for their hunger, are very difficult to feed. They may be starving by the millions but it would never occur to them to kill a cow and eat it. They would rather die. Eating in India is a complex affair with severe rules which may be hygienic, social, or religious in origin. A casual glance from an impure passer-by is enough to make their food inedible. Nor would a thirsty man ever drink from a vessel where another man has drunk before him. Our plates, glasses, and cutlery are obscene to him.

This film is dedicated entirely to Freddy, as an expression of my gratitude. I wanted to have some footage of him to remember him by. He helped me a great deal, from the very first day.

Kapila had gone. Freddy came over and sat near me very discreetly. As I lay on the ground in the shadow of a wall near the Ganges, a miracle was taking place inside me. A feeling of peace invaded me, so powerful that it made me weep. A feeling of peace and forgiveness. I was absolved from my past errors and mistakes. The weight of time and of my life had been lifted from me. Tranquil tears came all by themselves, without pain or sobs. Shedding them was sweet, like the sweetness of returning to the home of your childhood. An attempt to describe it would only betray it. Or should I call it sacred, but who dares use that word today? I wept because a man had looked at me.

Three days later, I had lost everything, even my suitcase.

Film 21 (dedicated to Kapila). A director once said to me, "If you want to reproduce a cannon on the screen, you must not use a real cannon. That would look fake. Rather, you must invent a cinematographic cannon, and only that will seem real."

Indeed, in this film, Kapila barely resembles himself. Where is his expression? His person? Only a great painter could do him justice.

But (I discovered this tonight) a great painter has already painted his portrait. This happened five centuries ago, at the end of 1485. The dark ascetic which Sandro Botticelli painted to the right of the Madonna de' Bardi, that is Kapila. The same face, thin build, hair, nose, beard, even the gestures of the hand and the mouth that is speaking, and especially the eyes with their mysterious gentleness.

Dawn. Kapila is awake. He has gone down to the Ganges to wait for the sun. Here is a close-up of him – legs crossed, immobile, straight, illuminated by the first rays of the sun, withdrawn into absolute meditation. You see, he does not even notice the flies walking on his face, his nostrils, or on the corner of his eyes. This entronaut is far away, beyond the power of earthly gravity, at an incalculable distance, heading towards that distant star whose happy vibration he bears. This is why his gaze can bring you peace.

Noon. Kapila is eating his one daily meal: two handfuls of boiled rice from a little metal bowl. Aside from the bowl, his only other possessions are the long bamboo pole of the pilgrim and the ochre cloth which he uses to cover himself and which he washes each day. He eats rice with his hands, the way we eat bread. He smiles and listens to the people sitting near him and plays with the squirrels. Do you see them? There are two of them: pretty, tiny, striped creatures. India is full of them. They scamper down from the trees quite confidently, but are not trusting enough to come within an arm's reach. But when Kapila passes by, they run to greet him, and jump up on him. There's always one on his shoulder. They say that this has happened ever since he was a hermit in the jungle. They call him Kapila of the squirrels.

Afternoon. Kapila surrounded by people asking advice – concerning the health of the body or the soul, the spiritual path, love, the family, injustice. Some seek a blessing, others only a glance. His answers are brief and taciturn. Some perform a gesture of merit and place two handfuls of boiled rice in the bowl which the ascetic will eat tomorrow. A woman hands him a piece of fruit which he will give to a child, and another a flower which he will take to the temple. In India the holy man must give advice: it is his social function. And in our own world this was once done, in the Christian centuries, at the time of the hermits.

Film 22. This is a confused sequence – in and out of trains. Yes, this is a third-class Indian carriage. 8 horse power, 40 men? No, 8 horse power and 100 men.

Three days after my experience, Kapila left the Ganges and went to the railway station in Benares. An old man I had never seen before walked along before him and Raman and Freddy walked behind him. I was next to the American and I was feeling very disturbed.

"Is he leaving?"

"I don't know."

"What are you going to do?"

"Follow him."

"I must speak to him."

"Come."

"Where? I left everything at the hotel: my suitcase, camera, cheques, passport. Where are you going?"

For the last two days I had been trying to talk to Kapila, but all in vain. In the morning it was impossible, he was absorbed in his meditations. Impossible in the afternoon because of the people all around him; how could I have told him the story of my experience with all those people around? Impossible in the evening. Rao came to get me with his tricycle and took me back to the hotel where I finally had something to eat. As I lay down to sleep, I promised myself that I would speak to him the next day.

And now he was leaving. I had no idea where – India is immense. No, I absolutely had to speak to him. The train was already puffing away in the station. Freddy asked Raman where they were going, Raman asked the old man who replied that he had invited Kapila to Agra, and showed them two tickets. Freddy and Raman ran to buy theirs and I ran after them to the ticket window.

"Freddy, I must speak to him. Tomorrow I'll come to Agra by plane."

"Tomorrow? But who knows where we'll be by then?"

"Freddy, what should I do?"

"I'm buying you a ticket. Have you ever travelled third class in India?"

He bought the ticket. When we reached our destination I would telegraph the hotel. He dragged me to the train and pushed me into a carriage which was already full, thus demonstrating the penetrability of bodies. But he did not manage to get on and disappeared, just as the others had vanished.

I found myself in the crowded mass of people,

crushed on every side, surrounded by a hundred heads at different heights. Overhead, men, women and children were sitting on the luggage racks, below me others sat huddled on the floor, or stretched in the aisles. Two hundred eyes were staring at me.

Film 23. (At the Taj Mahal in Agra.) At dawn I arrived in the city where a prince had built the most beautiful tomb in the world in honour of the woman he loved, uniting there astonishment and reverence, majesty and grace, waking and dream. I was exhausted after my ten-hour trip in the night in third class. Freddy got off a nearby carriage and came towards me with a big smile on his face. He had slept through the whole journey. Instead, I was a wreck, my eyes puffy, my mouth bitter, unshaven, cramps in the stomach, my intestines and bladder full, itching all over, my legs barely able to stand up and my feet swollen – hungry, thirsty, sleepy. I was in such bad shape that I could not even think about my anxiety concerning the things I had left in Benares, nor about the fear at finding myself there with only a few rupees in my pocket, a filthy shirt, a pair of shorts and some old sandals.

Freddy immediately took me in his charge. In the crowded station we could not find the others, but he knew where he could find them later on. He gave me something to drink, loaded me onto a tricycle and took me to the river where he undressed me, put me in the water, helped me wash, stretched me out in the sun, and then under the shade of a tree. He was so helpful he seemed like a son – Aeneas and Anchises. I made an effort to thank him and then instantly fell asleep. When I awoke I was alone.

The shadows of the trees had moved. I sat very still and watched the river flow. Hungry and penniless in the middle of India, I should have felt worried, and yet I was not. Instead, everything seemed quite unreal: the solitary place, the big river, the exotic vegetation, the spiritual perfection of the Taj Mahal on the horizon. No, it did not seem real, but rather the backdrop of a theatre, and my solitude was only a role that I was playing. But I was playing it badly, like an actor who at the dramatic moment sneers instead of despairing. Rather I burst out laughing, thinking how strange life was, and then, on another level, somewhere higher within me, I felt protected and safe in the destiny which I was fulfilling. Archangel, Archangel.

I was still sitting there calmly watching the river flow when Freddy arrived. He had organized everything. My luggage would be sent to my Italian friend Alberto, in Pondicherry. Freddy rested for awhile and smoked his pipe, and then said, "Italian, let's go see Kapila."

I got up, with a bit of a twisted neck for having slept on the sand.

"Tell me who Kapila is."

Who was this man who is now named Kapila? What was his name, what sort of life had he lived? No one knew anything about his past. They said that he had lived the four orthodox ages of the Indian. A student until the age of eighteen (studying Sanskrit, the language of the gods, Hindi, the language of men, and the three languages which the foreigners had brought to India: English, French, and Portugese); for another eighteen years he had been head of a family (wife, children, relatives, work), then a hermit for five years, with his wife, following the tradition (hut in the jungle where his wife died) and since that time a pilgrim without a name or ties, beyond illusion, anchored in the Supreme, wandering in the winds, the final phase. They call him Kapila of the squirrels, the Tantric master. In India the lack of a biography is wisdom.

I met Kapila as the sun was going down in a field near the Taj Mahal. Freddy left discreetly. Raman remained, for he sometimes functioned as interpreter. But I did not need him. Kapila's French was harmonious and unusual.

I had brought with me a swarm of ideas to say to him, but now that I was sitting before him I lacked courage. I did not want to bore him with my story, the story of my journeys, the people I had met, the Archangel, or the wind which had blown me all the way to Benares where I had found a gaze of peace. I could not bring myself to say these things, and was silent.

Perhaps he listened to my silence, and certainly he smiled at it. He was looking for the words which would be most suited to me. A squirrel scampered down his shoulder and rested in his hand, but a swooping hawk frightened it and made it run away. Kapila smiled.

"The squirrel is never a witness."

Perhaps he wasn't searching for the words which were best suited to me. Perhaps he was searching for the inner condition which gives the word something more than the power of persuasion: the power of illumination. He began: "There is a fable which says that God made a man of clay and set him on his feet, but he fell down. He tried again, but the man fell down again. In order to hold the clay man up, he went inside him. He is inside: he is the witness."

Another squirrel scampered up to him and he gave it an almond.

"He is never a witness. He is always compelled by hunger or fear."

I found again the tenderness of his eyes, more eloquent than any words. He continued slowly, searching for the right expression, repeating:

"Man is valid when he is a witness. Virtue? It is being the witness of one's own voracity and one's own fear: detach oneself, observe them, judge them, accept them or reject them. Intelligence? It means being the witness of one's own ideas, one's own thoughts: detach oneself, observe them, judge them, accept them or reject them. He who allows himself to be dragged along by his voracity has no virtue, he who allows himself to be dragged along by the first idea which comes into his head, has no intelligence. Detach yourself, strip yourself, step back and become the witness. If you strip yourself away, you are only a gaze."

I did not understand. I did not want fables; but rather the recipe for my ills. Words bubbled up inside me now, agitated I began to speak.

"He shaped us with clay? It is a poetic story but what good is it? If it was first made of clay, now it is granite and it is suffocating me. He is inside me? But where? Where, who has met him?"

He looked at me fraternally and said only, "You will meet him when you step back. He dwells in the depths of the heart and he looms above our head. It is not a fable. Open a crack in the clay."

His certainty persuaded me and yet it disturbed me. God dwells in me, then he is inside me? It was a disturbing thought and yet exalting. I got up and strode across the field. The unknown guest. The tropical sunset . . .

I began to run, urged by a fervour which was also fear. The infinite within my eight palms of clay. Once someone said to me, "Who chooses the infinite is chosen by the infinite." And this was truly awesome.

Films 24-30. (From the Taj-Mahal to Mahabalipur.)

We went from temple to temple, train to train, bus to bus, north to south, for two thousand kilometres, perhaps even more. How did I end up on this bizarre pilgrimage, improvised day by day, weary and difficult, under the tropical sun, among the miseries and the greatness of India? How did such a thing happen? I entrusted myself more and more to the Archangel.

This film shows only temples. I can only recognize a few of them. As for the others I do not remember their names. Perhaps I never knew them. There was a small group of us, never more than six or seven, following Kapila. Freddy and Raman were always there, others came and went.

I spoke very little. I was losing the habit of wasting myself in words. Silent among the taciturn, we communicated with a nod. I felt an inner strength growing within me which is normally lost in chatter.

I spoke little. The Indians ate rice, Freddy and I added a bit of fruit and milk to our diet. We possess the surprising ability to reduce our food consumption, and even abolish it, as happened to Teresa Neuman and Niccolo of Flue. My stomach problems vanished.

I slept little, wherever I was, often out of doors. I soon forgot about beds. Freddy gave me a little air mattress that I could wash with water. I woke up before sunrise, so as not to miss the dawn, which like sunset, is a special hour. At those two moments of the day, I enjoyed a chaste and primitive serenity. After sunset I often sat up late questioning Raman on the subject of love, essential for Tantra. The dialogue continued late into the Indian night, where the stars hang so low overhead you can almost touch them.

So I joined an unexpected pilgrimage, full of mystery and discomfort, under the skies of India, so poor and so great.

Until I fell ill.

Film 33. (Dedicated to Raman.) Raman, who knows where you are now? Raman, a feather-weight Bengali. The film shows you as you were when I met you, dressed in a sheet as white as your smile. Raman the interpreter of Kapila, Raman first a secondary character and later very important. Sometimes he looked twenty, at other times thirty. Raman gentle and secret, silent, ready to answer, ready to remain silent, initiated in the sacred rites which are based on love.

But a love unlike what we imagine, all closed in the soul, addressed to the divine, and yet women sense it. Wherever we stopped, Raman was the target of the long oblique glances of the young women. He did not notice.

Where are you now, Raman? Perhaps you are still following Kapila, or perhaps you have reached the Himalaya, as you wished, or perhaps your ashes have been scattered in the Ganges since the human form does not last long in India.

Our nightly dialogues: astonishing truths, archaic mysteries, dating back to the time of the paleolithic Venuses with their enormous breasts and bellies. The virile power, coiled like a serpent around the sacred vertebra. For the followers of Tantra, God is feminine. There, look at this shot. You see? That young girl, age fifteen, used to come every day to Kapila to offer him two handfuls of boiled rice. Most certainly her mother sent her. The offering of rice to a wise man is a gesture full of merit. I watch her fill the master's bowl, but she is not looking at it, her eyes are turned to Raman. This is extraordinary in a country like this one where women never look at men.

I would like to be as young as Raman . . .

Nightly dialogues.

Love as energy, without virtue or sin, as an electricity capable of enlightening or killing, love without carnality. For every lover on earth, love is a ritual of words and gestures. It is not carnal. Rather when the ritual is about to reach its peak, every lover forgets the body and flees from the senses, requires darkness and silence, closes his eyes, closes himself within, goes beyond the mind and projects himself into the blackness, and there in a supreme state of inner concentration, the transcendental joy explodes.

Flesh, mucus, glands have only offered the pretext and have helped this concentration of the spirit. Thus the bed becomes an altar and the palace a temple. Yet if the lovers are no longer in love, or if they are distracted or tired, and the encounter is only corporeal and the soul elsewhere, then the sublime concentration is missing and they rise from the act depressed and ashamed for they have lost a great opportunity. The man feels like a beast, the woman like a whore.

For the followers of Tantra, love is the conquest of supernatural power.

Now look at this scene. It is a street in a town. Here is our group. You see these two girls in the emerald and the amaranth saris? Watch closely, they overtake us. One turns to look at Raman and now turns to the other. Then they laugh together. It is a common scene in Paris, but in India it is incredible. Raman does not notice, and yet he is young, at the most, thirty years old. Kapila smiles at him and remembers the divine Krishna who made the young shepherdesses fall in love with him. It must be that if virgins attract men, then chaste men attract women.

Nightly dialogue.

"Raman, if love brings divine joy, why are you chaste?"

"With that act you touch paradise for an instant and then you fall back to earth. Through renunciation you touch paradise and bring it down to earth."

"Paradise on earth? Is it possible?"

"It's true: a continual, intense joy, marvellous, more real than the real, more concrete than the body, more delightful than every delight, more real than air, ananda, the inexhaustible joy, the perfect joy, the joy."

"Raman, I envy you."

"Kapila will help you break the clay. He will help you."

Films 37-41. (Dedicated to me.) Freddy shot these and they are far superior to my own. The frames are excellent, the colour and movement good. I even suspect that Freddy used to work in the movies in the past. No, no, he said. He doesn't like to remember the past. As for his scars, he has mentioned some war in the jungle to me, though I don't know if it was Korea or Vietnam. Thanks to these scars he has a military pension, which in India is quite enough for him, living as he does, a wandering ascetic.

I owe it to Freddy if I have these films in which I see myself. But I don't like myself. My physical form is alien to me. The face in particular, but also the rest. I have never recognized myself in this form. In India even less, intent as I was in separating myself from myself, stepping back, so I could break the clay.

I was by the sea when the clay broke. It was the 12th of April. Film 41 goes as far as the evening prior to this experience. The other films, from 37 on, are merely the preamble.

Film 37. I am climbing on to a bus along with Kapila.

Westerners are wrong to reject these buses. They are punctual, you are guaranteed a seat and they cost little. My baggage has been reduced to a knapsack. My suitcase is with my friends in Pondicherry who sent my money, documents and tickets on to me.

I am sitting next to Kapila. After our talk in the field, we have spoken together only a few times. I have asked him a couple of questions and he has given me a few suggestions. He is a master not because of what he preaches (he never preaches) but for what he communicates, thanks to a hidden osmosis of souls. I have come to realize that we are not closed oysters, rather we are open on all sides, sensitive to the vibrations of others. The vibration of Kapila elevates me.

In the bus I tell him about dawn and sunset, those moments when I am invaded by a feeling of vast serenity. He looks at me and seems pleased.

Then, "Keep your serenity day and night."

"Day and night? How?"

"Step back."

Film 38. Yes, I am ridiculous dressed in that outfit. My shorts and shirt are tattered. My suitcase is in Pondicherry, and I have no changes of clothes in my knapsack and in the villages we have visited I certainly haven't seen any western clothes to buy. Freddy took pity on me, and gave me a dhoti, a piece of cloth which the Indians skilfully wrap around themselves to make trousers and a tunic, requiring no sewing, buttons or pins. But this dhoti keeps falling off – I may end up naked at any moment. So Freddy, pipe in his mouth, cuts the cloth and makes me a little skirt with a belt and a scarf to protect my shoulders and head from the sun. Here is the result. I am ridiculous, but I am comfortable and so who cares? In India no one would turn around to look and see how a man was dressed or if he was naked. Tropical nudity is far removed from the concepts of nudism or striptease.

"Keep your serenity day and night." It is very difficult. While contemplating dawn or sunset, my soul becomes limpid, smooth and blue as a mountain lake. It is not only a tenuous feeling, it is a solid state of being. But as soon as it is finished, my inner state changes. I speak with Raman, prepare my knapsack, look at the people on the street, and then I am projected into that activity, forgetting that I have a serenity to keep, completely absorbed in my everyday thoughts and habitual gestures. Later I remember, "Keep your serenity." I remember and I feel irritated with myself because I have forgotten. But irritation is not serenity and for the rest of the time the smallest things plunge me into oblivion, getting on a train, or buying a piece of fruit, looking to see where the others have gone.

"What should I do?"

"Step back."

This is the secret. You must step back, separate yourself from your everyday thoughts and habitual gestures: look at them. It is patient work, like the work of the watchmaker who observes the spirals and gears under his lens, cleans, and calibrates. The secret is to retreat deep into oneself until one encounters an almost imperceptible vibration, which then becomes more and more evident, a silent, separate and calm vibration. He who anchors himself in this possesses serenity all day long. And the night?

Film 39. You might think it was an erotic film. Freddy spying on me caught me when I visited the bas-reliefs of the temple, where all the gestures, poses, caresses, enraptured smiles, ardent faces, and pleasures of love are represented. Love has transfigured these lovers and the pleasure of the body into an altar.

It is an isolated and ancient temple on a white plain, inhabited by a holy man, almost completely naked. He has taken the vow of silence and greets us with palms joined, smiles for a minute and then disappears. A group of women arrive from a nearby village, old women and young girls, a sick woman, and a pregnant one. They go into the temple to venerate the lingam, surround it with floral garlands, sprinkle it with coloured powders, and light sticks of incense around it. Their gestures are chaste, they do not know what the word erotic means and they could not imagine. Eros is a god and love is sacred.

The group of women walk away across the white plain, their coloured saris fluttering in the breeze. These people do not have our sense of sin, for them it is unthinkable to be at odds with God. They do not have our taste for sin, for one's own sins, which we find so fascinating, or for the sins of others which make us feel virtuous and indignant.

For Freddy sin is good humour. Born and raised a Presbyterian, become a murderer out of military duty, reaching India somehow, he finds it amusing to film a Catholic surrounded by statues which for the Indians are sacred but for the Christians are obscene.

Look at this shot, I seem to be absorbed in some wanton thought. Rather I am thinking about something completely different, and feel quite discouraged.

I have discovered someone inside me that I never knew was there. A tiny and intolerable me. I discovered it by chance. Kapila had called me aside to say something to me. I was serene, in tune with the vibration which I had felt since the morning which I had discovered in stepping back and in which I had anchored myself. When I left the master, I saw Raman looking at us questioningly from the distance and for a second I felt triumphant. Kapila had called me and not them. An expression of satisfaction appeared on my lips. I was shocked as I looked at myself inside. "Is it possible that I am so petty?" It was the first discovery. Many more followed.

For example, at meals if I have two pieces of fruit and I offer one to someone else, the individual inside me keeps the nicer piece for himself and gives the other one away. When speaking in a group, he always wants to intervene, to give his opinion and show off. When I buy something he counts the change, convinced that the others are thieves. He compares me to the other people I meet, praising me, saying how intelligent I am, how content I am with myself. When face to face with a mirror he even dares to say I am handsome – though reduced to my present state (look at me in the film), thin, tattered, and dressed in rags. Shameless he even says, "That lovely girl isn't looking at Raman, she is looking at you." And if the subject of my books comes up during the conversation, I become a turkey gurgling with satisfaction.

But this is nothing. I am angry and cruel. If I hurt my shinbone I feel like taking it out on some poor dog in the street by giving him a kick.

I will say no more. This frightened me. Greed and fear alternate in me because I ask myself at every movement, "Will it be to my advantage or disadvantage?". There is no vileness which does not attract him, no perversion that does not excite him. He has always been there inside me, cohabited with me, but only now have I begun to see his face.

Kapila listens to all I have to say while the lovers in

the bas-reliefs look at us. Then he shows me a method.

"If you concentrate on him, you give him life. Remain firm in your serenity and pay no attention. Without your strength he will wither and die."

Film 40. Filmed inside the temple, by firelight. This film is all shadows. Hardly anything can be seen. I can recognize the sequence of the serpent ritual in these images only because I witnessed it.

The protagonist is Raman, naked, sitting cross-legged, his body straight, his head bent, his eyes staring at the wall, his eyes on the sculptured scenes which he seems to be a part of, as he is so bronze and immobile. Kapila is sitting opposite him in this same pose, his body a lighter colour, gold, an ancient marble statue, his eyes closed. On his lips, the ineffable inner smile of the East, the smile you may find on the faces of all entronauts, heroes and gods.

The sacred fire leaps high in the brazier. In the firelight the two men turn to stone while the figures sculptured on the wall come alive. The figures of the lovers seem to move in the leaping light of the flames. The females offer their round breasts, their hips, their thighs. Mouths kiss, skilled fingers caress. The men clutch the women ardently and a thousand living bodies undulate along the walls. Kapila is the silent guide, but Raman is the protagonist, completely surrounded by the Dionysiac scene. Surrounded but not penetrated by it. His detachment from this earthly attraction is so strong that he can look at this Bacchanal without losing his serenity. The slightest participation on his part would be immediately revealed by his naked body.

Immobile, burning with the inner creative fire which is curled like a snake around the base of his spine, he guides it vertebra by vertebra up to his epiphysis. A long shudder flickers up his spine.

Raman is stone; he does not breathe. He has gone beyond the stars. The chaste hero has defeated the terrestrial orgy.

Film. 41. Last film. It is dawn. We arrive in Mahabalipur, sixty kilometres from Madras, today April 11.

A famous place with monolithic architecture. The kings of Pallava, gigantic animals in living rock, the heroes of the epic of Krishna, a place for western tourists and museum-maniacs. There is a whole bus full of Germans.

Rather it is a sacred place for Kapila, who knows how to read in these granite slabs the universal story of the Bhagavad Gita, who knows how to find the presence of Shiva in these caves. Kapila, always so contained, grows fervid before the long wall of rock where gods, men and animals are portrayed running joyfully to drink the waters of the Ganges. He points out these figures to me.

"Look, these beings are all enraptured by the divine joy, ananda, ananda. Whoever has experienced it will find it again, ananda, ananda."

While he is speaking to me, two German archaeologists (or mineralogists or who knows what) are picking up stones, measuring the statues, examining the granite, discussing its composition. They cannot imagine that which is so evident to Kapila's eyes. Those who are absorbed by the body cannot see the spirit, and those who are absorbed by the spirit cannot see the body. A corporeal civilization is necessarily atheist.

Monumental Mahabalipur does not speak to me. It remains silent. Perhaps I am too worried about becoming an apprentice entronaut. A difficult task, with no repose, day or night.

I must keep my serene vibration which is so easy to lose. I must speak with my Archangel and I must keep watch on my underground cohabitant, so wicked and filthy. I must maintain this subtle breeze which wafts down from above (from the nape of my neck) fresh and full of oxygen, miraculous. I must close myself to visionary temptations, to the limbos and to the hells which sometimes crack open when you attempt to evolve within. I must conquer the night because my sleep has changed and sometimes I find a transparency in which serenity accompanies me until the morning. I must go deeper into my new discovery that I am not myself. And finally I must watch over the fire, those inner ardent fires of devotion and abandonment though I don't know to whom; perhaps to God, if this word were not so worn out, so wasted, perhaps to the divine mother, the ancient, primeval, paleolithic, eternal, and divine mother. Perhaps I must erase myself and become her instrument.

My friend, do you believe I am mad? For every caveman the astronaut is mad.

I know quite well that the spiritual forces are not consoling abstractions or effusive sentiments, they are powerful realities, even terrible. But with Kapila I am like a little boy led by the hand.

This is the last scene of Film 41. Intense colours. Radiant sky, azure sea, white foam on the waves, yellow beach where we walk along, our feet sinking into the sand. Kapila (ochre); Raman (bronze), and I (flesh coloured). Freddy does not appear. He is managing the camera. Three coloured spots are advancing towards the Temple on the Shore. There it is. Very tiny, compared to some of God's skyscrapers. But it is as perfect as the Parthenon, or as the Taj Mahal, though very different. The millennia have coloured it with rust, prayers have consecrated it, God has blessed it. Near the sea, far from the world, uninhabited. We are the only presence except for the immense peace all around us. The last few frames show me as I stop to admire it.

The last film, the last testimony. For everything that followed I have only a handful of photographs, and few notes, and my memories confided to a dictaphone.

I stop and admire, then remove my cloth and plunge into the sea. It is the Indian Ocean. Freddy imitates me, an expert swimmer, and swims far from the shore. I look at the temple from the water – it is very near, almost on the water's edge. I feel its power. I feel that I have reached a milestone. I will stop here, I have arrived. A few profane places have sometimes given me this same impression: for example many years ago when I first stepped off the boat in Capri. Here is the place I will remain. But here this impression is much stronger, not a profane aesthetic landscape, but rather arcane, sacred, and overwhelming. This is where my pilgrimage ends.

I emerge from the sea dripping wet and say impulsively to Kapila:

"I want to stay here."

He agreed immediately. Freddy arrived and took on the task of finding someone to bring me food and water from the village each day. Raman assured me that they would come back for me in ten days. I had expected resistance, but instead, as soon as I expressed this wish, a mechanism was set in motion, encountering no friction. This surprised me and left me feeling somewhat uncertain.

We ate in the shadow of the temple. When the sun had begun to wane a bit, we got ready to leave. The time was drawing near when I would be left alone.

Suddenly I was seized by anxiety. I had been liberated from this feeling for so long that I hardly remembered what it was like. I approached Kapila:

"You will come back?"

A little voice in me had suggested that I would never see him again. Horrified by this thought, I gathered up my mattress and my knapsack. No, I will not leave him, I will not remain here. His serene eyes penetrated my fear and dissolved it. Childishly I made my claim on him, "You must initiate me into the serpent ritual."

He smiled and denied this. "No, it is not for you. For you power does not rise from below, it descends from on high. Do not fear, I will always be near you."

He left me with these mysterious words. They set out on their way. I watched as their figures grew tiny in the distance. Freddy turned to wave goodbye. Then they vanished in the eternity of time, in the immensity of India.

"You're a bit mad, really a bit mad."

If this woman who cares for me could have come from Europe and seen me there, naked and alone in the night, in the niche of a temple sitting beside the column of the lingam. If she could have seen me sleepless, my eyes opened wide on the dark roaring ocean, if she could have seen my gaunt face, my emaciated body, the sores on my feet, she would have burst out weeping and run to assist me, sobbing that I had finally gone completely insane.

I asked myself if that was not what had happened. Between the sea and the nocturnal sky, I debated this question and concluded, in a loud voice:

"No, what have I left? I was a slave to pettiness, greed, and fear, a restless man, dissatisfied with my life and frightened by death. What have I found? I have found peace instead of restlessness, serenity instead of fear, I have found the search and not the void, and hope instead of disgust. I have found the divine. Thus I am not mad, I am practical, concrete, pragmatic, and full of good sense."

The sea, the night, the sky agreed with me. I went to sleep.

Punctually at dawn I woke up. It was the 12th of April. My mattress had deflated during the night, but I had slept well. I washed myself in the sea and went back to shore to watch the sunrise on the beach.

At the very instant the sun appeared, above my head a boundary opened, a dam broke, and from on high joy flooded down upon me. It penetrated me, filled me, and surrounded me. A delight I had never felt before, an enrapturing inebriating river, an impulse of grace, a sparkling pleasure within my pallidness. How can I describe it? But how can I refrain from speaking of it?

I could not stand up, so I lay down on the sand immobile, astonished, struck dumb by the miracle, unable to believe that such a thing could be happening to me, as I was so undeserving. I closed my eyes and abandoned myself, melted by this powerful joy ananda, ananda, I abandoned myself to certainty, certainty. Finally. How shall I describe and how can I be silent?

It lasted a week, I believe, though each day it diminished slightly. I did not count the days. I only know that a little girl came to bring me food and drink (Freddy had seen to this). Dumb as I was, oblivious, almost outside my body – at first I could barely eat and the little girl, mercifully helped me. She was dark-skinned with shining eyes and a ready smile. The slenderness of her hips made her resemble more a young boy. She abounded in cheerfulness like all

Indians in their childhood and early youth. The mystery of India is not hunger, but joy.

Then she brought her brother, then her mother, her father, and her whole family. Then one day I realized that they had mistaken me for a saint or a sage and they venerated me. Hunger and troubles had taught them to glimpse the inner man, free and happy. Thus they come running at the first sign. I tried to dissuade them, but they only venerated me all the more. I fled that very night. The mystery of India is not hunger, it is joy.

I fled towards Pondicherry. I had to speak to someone. I was returning into myself, that bitter condemnation. My mind had begun to reason, to converse, to seek out plausible explanations, and piled everything up within its boundaries. This was quite painful to me. In Pondicherry I was sure to find someone who could translate my recent experiences to my mind and somehow calm it. Intellectuals suffer from mental hypertrophy, just as athletes suffer from muscular hypertrophy. From Pondicherry I would return to the Temple on the Shore for my appointment with Kapila. This was my plan but things did not work out that way.

I reached Madras by bus, I believe. My memory is very confused. I already had a fever. I remember going into a shop in Madras to buy some shorts and a shirt. I could not arrive in Pondicherry wearing the little skirt that Freddy had made me in which the tears at the back revealed my buttocks. I remember that I took a train, but this is confused in my mind with a dream in which I was running after a train but couldn't reach it because I had too much luggage. Then after letting everything fall, I managed to jump on the last car.

I don't resist fevers very well. If any temperature goes over thirty-eight degrees centigrade, my mind begins to wander. In Madras I realized I needed to seek treatment, and so I pushed on to Pondicherry where there was a new hospital and a clinic run by French nuns, and where, most especially, Alberto was, and my other friends and my suitcase.

I took the train but never arrived. I got off half way, leaving my knapsack, mattress, passport, plane ticket, dollars and rupees in the train. At that point I must have had a fever of about 40 degrees. Why had I got off the train? Who knows? I don't even remember that I went over and lay down in the shade of a tree and that a few peasants found me and called the road guard who watched over the transport of rice. He ordered that I should be taken to a hut and there I opened my eyes.

I was cold and shivering. I lay on the ground on a straw mat. A woman sat crouching next to me. I could see her hands – worn out, the palms of her hands hard and withered, her fingers knotty and thin, her hands furrowed by the thick veins which protruded – poor veins of tired, cold blood trying to push themselves out and warm themselves in the sun.

Of those hours I remember hardly anything, except a delirious scene in which I laughed a lot: I was speaking to Essy about peyote and Maggie about omnipotence while Nala and Poo, mere children, gravely listened to the dervish who was saying, no salad without the elevator and I nearly burst my sides laughing.

I opened my eyes and found myself looking at Freddy with his red hair, his freckles, his wink, his kind smile and his encouraging words. "Italian, what are you doing here?" I was so confused and relieved that I began to cry, unable to speak. Freddy, my friend, how unjust I have been towards you, when I condemned you in my heart because you lived like an American vagabond, with your pipe. Once when you photographed me near the statues of the lovers I even called you a Presbyterian murderer. American, my friend, stupid as I am, I did not understand that your path lies in being fluid, and that is your way of breaking the clay. I cried without restraint, incapable of thanking him, incapable of asking him how he had found me.

He took me in his arms, as he had done in Agra, and laid me in an ox cart. Aeneas and Anchises. Then transferred me to an automobile, and finally laid me in a hospital bed in Pondicherry where Alberto, already informed as to what had happened, was waiting for me. My passport and ticket had already been found. Freddy did not stay long. He hurriedly gave me a little bronze Ganesh, a gift from Kapila, laid his hand on my shoulder and said, "Italian, get well soon," and left, tall and robust, full of naturalness in his loincloth, striding down the corridor among the doctors in their white jackets.

Though I was so weak I could not speak, I was glad to find the softness of that bed. Grateful, I smiled at my Archangel.

They treated me with their approximative hygiene and I was soon well again. They ordered me to return to Europe to recover. The head physician came to tell me this in person. I did not answer or discuss it. Leave Kapila? Never. I was silent. This was my business, not the doctors'. I invited Alberto to continue his conversation.

I had told him what it was that had urged me to head towards Pondicherry, on the way. Just as there are people who seek cures for their rheumatism or kidney stones in the spring waters of faraway places, I had come to Pondicherry, a place in which the confused western mind may find clarification concerning the spiritual paths of the East. This and that had happened to me. What was I supposed to make of it?

I needed an injection of ideas to help me understand, as my mind was so saturated with western explanations.

I slowly recovered in that veiled April. I recited Italian poetry and the nurses laughed. In India April is intense, but I felt weak and languid. Alberto spoke and I listened weakly.

He gave me the dose. He spoke of the joy, the transforming, supreme-transcendent, divine, unique joy of which all other forms are only the pale imitation. The joy which each of us seeks but never finds, and thus we have no peace. From his tone of voice I understood that we had both experienced it and were brothers. We had experienced that unchangeable joy which does not age with time, which the body does not stain, which gives you certainty and saves you from solitude. Joy, not in a posthumous and fleeting paradise, but here on this earth, in this body.

We were in the ward. He spoke softly in Italian near my pillow, and the other patients were silent, almost as though they could understand our conversation. "It's true, Alberto, it's true." He said, "Having encountered it only once, for only a moment, changes you for ever and you will never forget it. Having it perpetually in oneself transforms life into Eden. This joy is the substratum of the universe and justifies its existence." I agreed, my mind calmed, "It's true, Alberto, it's true."

I was cured and I owe this testimony to India: its secret is joy, I owe this testimony to all those who gave me their help and assistance: its secret is joy; if my name burdens you, throw it away, but keep the song.

They forced me to leave – Alberto was the first. "You're in bad shape, you must look after yourself, the hot weather is approaching. Europe is beautiful in May. Who knows where Kapila is? You won't be able to find him in your current state." But the last push was this:

"Don't forget that you are a Christian."

"Alberto, what are you saying? I am a Hindu."

"You don't become Hindu, you are born Hindu."

"Alberto, *you* are telling me this?"

"It's not mere chance that we were baptized. Your Archangel comes straight from Maggie's Gospel."

I did not want to argue, I was too weak. More than my head, my legs agreed with him, so weak as they were. I received telegrams from Rome urging me to return. Kapila had said, "I will always be near you." I had with me his little bronze Ganesh.

After an endless flight, the captain announced that we were in the sky over Greece, above Mount Athos, heading towards Rome.

JOURNEY TO
MOUNT ATHOS

What do I hope to find in Mount Athos? I ask myself this question as I am walking up the ramp to the plane which in one hour will take me from Rome to Athens. Despite the many obstacles I have encountered along the way, an incredible stroke of good luck has unexpectedly made this trip possible. Good luck? No, it was my Archangel's doing.

I find my seat, sit down, fasten my seat belt and begin musing things over. So I am on my way to Mount Athos because someone once told me (I don't know who, when, or why), because someone once told me (but people will tell you all sorts of things), someone once told me, perhaps during my trip back from India while flying over Greece, because someone once told me . . . I can't remember what they said. Perhaps no one told me anything at all. Perhaps I made it all up.

Or perhaps I said it and repeated it to everyone I met. In America, to the nudist Sam, to the California scientists, to Essy the peyote girl, and in Europe to omnipotent Maggie, to the aerosomatic Leroys.

What had I told them? Simply that I was going to visit the entronauts on Mount Athos.

"But there aren't any. Don't fool yourself. You've always had your head in the clouds."

This is what a friend of mine told me, an antique

dealer, expert in Byzantine art who wanted to warn me. He had once visited there and knew all about it. He is one of those people who treat you roughly when they care for you.

"I bet you believe in that Mount Athos where they pull you up with ropes. Right? Well, you're all wrong. You are confused. That was Meteora, which was something quite different. In Meteora the monasteries have been abandoned, it's a place for tourists. Are you interested in Byzantine art? No? Then why are you going to Mount Athos?"

John, a colleague, a reporter for a foreign newspaper, began to sneer when I confided my plans to him.

"Mount Athos? You know no females are allowed in: not even cows, or she-goats or bitches or mares. No females of any species. So keep your pants on."

A prelate also tried to discourage me. He was a very learned man, an expert in the subject of the history of Christianity. I must confess that people who are exceptionally learned in one particular field usually remind me of athletes – the deformed legs of football players, the monstrous shoulders of weight lifters.

He said, "Mount Athos. An interesting place. The monasteries there are in possession of some very ancient documents which have never been published. But it's very far away. It will take you at least a week to get there. On Mount Athos, they live in the year 1000. There are no roads; you must go about on foot or by mule. No electricity, nothing. The year 1000. Are you interested in the history of Christianity?"

I am ashamed to say no. His puzzled expression is eloquent. "So why are you going?"

Now in flight, I ask myself this same question. What is it I expect to find?

The plane is huge, an Olympic transatlantic. It has just arrived from New York and will continue on to Athens. I owe my ticket on this plane to a stunning stroke of good luck which occurred right before my departure. I mean, I owe it to my Archangel.

I had quite a hard time obtaining permission to visit Mount Athos. First of all, it is not a mountain, but a peninsula, not governed by Greece, but by a Greek theocracy which has been independent for a thousand years. You must have a visa and you must make an application explaining the reason for your visit. What should I have written on the forms? That I was looking for entronauts? I put down *profession: writer*. At that point my application began its long bureaucratic journey from the Greek embassy in Rome to the ministry in Athens, then to the offices in Thessalonika, on to the patriarchate of Constantinople, back to Athens, and then back to Rome. It will take nearly a month, so please take care of it, will you, Archangel?

He does indeed take care of it. In a few days everything is ready, thanks to a moment of inspiration. I suddenly thought of asking Umberto, a colleague of mine from Rome, a powerful man, for some advice.

"Where did you say you want to go? To Greece? I am trying to find someone to go there for me. Ring the embassy immediately. It doesn't matter if it's late. Ring Zaccaria and tell him you're the one I'm sending to Greece."

Zaccaria is a delightful person, calm, smiling, soft-spoken. He offers me *papastratos* and then takes me to lunch, thanking me for having accepted his invitation to visit Greece. Two colleagues of his are also coming on the trip. Would I mind visiting Athens? Would I mind visiting Olympia?

I suggest timidly, "Actually I'd like to visit Mount Athos."

"But of course, we'll take care of everything, your ticket, permission, lodging."

And that's how it all worked out. It was quite extraordinary. Archangel, Archangel.

A village doctor I used to know once complained, "If I cure my patients, they say it was the work of the Madonna, if they die, then people say it's my fault." I must give credit where it's due and give my thanks to the Archangel, Umberto, and Zaccaria.

Why am I going to Mount Athos? Because of a rite which took place many years ago, in a little chapel that no longer exists, in a village which no longer exists. The chapel has become a large church and the village has become a town. It was a baptism. My own baptism. The priest who performed the ceremony is dead, my godfather who repeated the formula is dead, my father who held me in his arms is dead, and all the others who stood around smiling that day are gone. There is no living trace left of that ceremony. I remember nothing about it, nor have I ever concretely felt the bond that it established. And yet if I am on my way to Mount Athos, it is because of that water, that rite, because of those people who made me Christian.

I have travelled all over the world in search of entronauts, those who seek the path in the names of Mohammed, Krishna, Buddha, Tantra or Aurobindo, or even in their own name or in no one's name. But somewhere there must be people who have encountered the sacred in the name of Christ.

While the plane is descending over Greece, I tell myself that I am going to Mount Athos because I am a Christian and this seems to me a good, noble, and true reason. I would be convinced of it, if it were less noble. Noble sentiments are freshly painted tombs.

They call it the sacred mountain. I am not going because of my baptism, nor am I going because I promised my director that I would. After so many long journeys, it would not be difficult to convince him to abandon the idea of this last stop.

I am going to Mount Athos because I cannot do otherwise. I am compelled to go. Life has always compelled me in one direction or another. I have not chosen to act, I have been obliged to do so. Some people claim, "That year, I decided to do this or that." They are lying but they do not realize it. Man believes he is free but in reality he is obliged to act. With the carrot dangling in front of his nose and the stick behind him, he is attracted by some things and prodded forward by others. How can he choose or decide? Hope draws me on towards Athens, pain prods me from behind.

When I left India and returned to Europe, I felt as though I had returned to a madhouse. The inner equilibrium I had established was now shattered. In India I had found a new, fresh, delicate sensitivity towards life, which was unsuited to the harshness of the West. I could not bear to read newspapers, listen to the radio, watch television, or go to the theatre. I did not recognize my city and found it hostile.

It was a city of fear: fear of the bomb, of insurrection, of cancer, of accidents, of murder, all illustrated with pictures in the news and repeated day in and day out until you were terrified out of your wits, along with everyone else. A city of violence, aggressive drivers, cursing pedestrians, knife-fights for a parking space, implacable hatred among individuals and groups, and for entertainment: a shoot-out at the cinema, or frenzied screaming at the stadium. A city of satyric furors: female nudity everywhere, women constantly on heat, men on the make, sex omnipresent.

In such a cosmos of frenetic vibrations, I lost all inner well-being, serenity, presence, or joy. The knowledge I had gained of inner techniques (the control of breath, awareness, and the mind) was useless to me. I became one of the anxious crowd, and my wicked cohabitant emerged triumphant from the depths and sat himself upon the throne.

But sometimes at sunset, locked in my room, staring at my little statue of Ganesh, I managed to find a few moments of Kapila's peace. Rare moments. The other days I suffered in the vibration of those forgotten wave lengths. They brought me pain, pain in my soul, so sharp that I could not bear it, throughout my whole being and physical body.

Return to India? Impossible, with no money, and so many commitments here in Europe. So then, why not try Mount Athos, complete the series of articles I had promised my director and find a few brief moments of serenity?

Even the woman who is always claiming, "You're a bit mad, really a bit mad", agreed. This time she said, "Go to Athens. It would do you good to get away from here for awhile."

It is these feelings of loss and hope which now urge me on towards Athos. Somewhere there must be people who have encountered the sacred in the name of Christ. If Athos is still a living mountain.

In Athens they have booked me a room in a *grand hotel*, where my two colleagues are also staying along with a young Greek writer, Milena, who has arrived on the same flight with me. She resembles a greyhound: tall and thin, a long stride, a sweet expression, and a fresh smile.

The four of us are having lunch together. The greyhound asks, "Why are you going to Mount Athos?"

I swallow a mouthful of food and say the first thing that comes into my head, "To meet the anchorites."

At that moment a memory emerges from the black depths of my mind, a memory I had utterly forgotten, the hidden persuader which had urged me to make this journey. I finally understand why I am going to Mount Athos. Someone (I don't know when or where or who) once said to me, "In Mount Athos, you will find the last hermits, the true Christian anchorites, the ancient ones, the ones portrayed with long hair and long beards, emaciated, with the bones of the dead. The ones who tamed the wild beasts of the Middle Ages. You must not miss it. It is perhaps the only place where you can still find them. They have inhabited the sacred mountain for over one thousand years without interruption. For twenty centuries they have been living in the same forests and caves, the masters with their disciples in an unbroken chain of a hundred generations. You must not miss it."

How could I have forgotten this irresistible reason? A reason much greater than myself, as vast as a continent. Ten entronauts would have been enough to save Sodom and Gomorrah, but at the time they could not be found. To save Europe, only ten entronauts are needed to keep the door open to joy, which is the aim of man.

Milena, unknowing and cruel, "Visit the anchorites? There haven't been any for the last fifty years!"

Athens is a modern capital, far too modern for those who cherish in their hearts the memory of the Hellenic marbles (beyond time). Here time has wreaked havoc. The Parthenon has been used as a house for courtesans, as a Christian church with a bell tower, as a mosque with a minaret, as a powder-magazine for the Ottoman Turks (which exploded), and as a marble quarry for thieves. What was left of it finally collapsed in an earthquake, yet the Parthenon still stands on the Acropolis, erect, but empty. An archaeological site. The soul of Athens is now to be found elsewhere.

This soul is hidden if you drive through the city. To see it, you must wait until evening, and then go on foot to visit the Plaka, the quarter where the taverns and eating places are located. I took Milena as my guide.

Narrow streets with steps up and down the Plaka, crowded with small tables, people passing by, young couples arm-in-arm. The girls in Athens are lovely, and Milena is beautiful in her wig, with her jewels and her shawl, with the charm women have when they are dressed for the evening. It is lovely to look at her.

I try to bring up the subject of Mount Athos. How does she know that there are no longer any hermits? She ignores my question, distracted by the food. The taste of the retsina at first astonishes you and then convinces you. Greek food too is surprising, with its unexpected and unusual alliances of flavours and aromas.

Then Milena tries to bring up the subject of politics. Now I pretend to be distracted by the food. Politics no, I cannot bear the hypocrisy, the continual pretence of noble sentiments for the people, the workers, freedom, justice, etc. They care nothing for these and do not dare admit that it is really the idea of power which intoxicates them. So why are they ashamed to admit it? Do you like power, do you want it? Then take it and stop talking about justice, the workers and freedom.

Don't deceive the people who believe in you. Take the power and keep it as long as it lasts and suffer, because power makes man ugly and destroys him.

No anchorites and no politicians. We are equal. The guitarist in the tavern has begun to sing. These are not the songs currently popular in other places. They are as Greek and as unusual as the food and the wine. Slow songs, the words barely pronounced, heart-rending. So the starry night is soon tinged with melancholy, the soul of Athens.

Now on another plane, on my way from Athens to Thessalonika, heading towards Mount Athos. During my recent visits to Olympia I asked people now and then, "Are there still anchorites on Mount Athos?"

"Anchorites?"

In Olympia the Greek games were quite different from our modern Olympics. Those were as true and sacred as ours are profane. False Hellenic antiquity. False medieval chivalry. Benares was Olympia. I found there the same temples, the same gods, the same principles, the same models. The wisdom of Ganesh is the wisdom of the Centaur, both are part man, part beast. The Acherloo is like the Ganges. The venerated phallus is the lingam. Olympia is an archaeological Benares. Maggie McCann and her angels are closer to Olympia than Baron de Coubertin and his flames.

In Olympia I met an elderly Orthodox priest who was visiting the ruins of the ancient sanctuaries. I immediately asked him, "Are there still anchorites on Mount Athos?"

He looked at me in astonishment, engrossed as he was in inspecting the ruins. Then he smiled kindly, quite happy to talk to me in French.

"So you are going to the Mount? Very fortunate, very fortunate for you indeed. It is a marvellous place. You will see such beautiful monasteries. Byzantine art . . . the history of Christianity . . . are you a historian?"

"Are there still hermits there?"

Perhaps he didn't understand, or perhaps he didn't know, or perhaps he didn't want to say. He seemed awkward.

"Hermits? They are all hermits on Mount Athos. Those who have been there have understood what holiness is."

I replied coldly, "Rasputin once visited there."

This priest was shattering my hopes. I wanted to tell him: No, monsignor, I am not interested in either history or art. Those are illusions, frivolous pastimes. I am searching for reality. If I wanted to see monasteries I could have stayed in Italy. So Milena is right. You have let the last Christian anchorite die, the last of one hundred generations is dead, and no one wept for this loss.

But I was silent. I did not call him monsignor because I knew it would offend him. I let him show me the ruins and prattle on to me about pagan myths. He believed that they were fables illustrating natural phenomenon. It saddened me to discover that a religious man could be so irreligious. This man preached the teachings of Jesus, but was unaware that myth is the only way to express the appearance of the sacred on the earth (the incarnation of Christ), unaware that myth provides the model for human behaviour and renders it meaningful (the imitation of Christ), unaware that only myth may give us hope and elevate us (the resurrection of Christ). What is a myth? Not a fable, but a supreme reality, narrated through a parable, which could not be narrated in any other way.

Are there still anchorites on Mount Athos?

I will know soon. The plane is about to land in Thessalonika.

Zaccaria's protection has followed me everywhere, guided me, and found me hospitality in Athens and now in Thessalonika. At the airport gate, a young woman was waiting for me. Thessalonika, we find this city mentioned in the Acts and epistles of the apostles. Thessalonika was the sister of Alexander for whom the city was named.

Sula works for the tourist office. However did people manage to travel before these institutions were created? She takes care of everything with a smile; she finds my bags, obtains a car, takes me to the hotel. I abandon myself in the arms of this comfort and bless Sula, Zaccaria and the Archangel. I only hope they aren't tired of working miracles.

Many people dislike grand hotels, and believe that they are all alike, all unoriginal, with terrible "international" cuisine. I, on the contrary, find them very comfortable; I hardly ever stay in them, because they are so expensive, but I am quite glad whenever I happen to end up in one. I find it very pleasant to chatter away to the concierge in my own language, to sink deep into the armchairs of the hall and observe the high life passing by, to be waited on by the maître, and to find a luminous reading lamp at my bedside so that I may sit up with a book at night. It's true that when the windows are closed, you do not know whether you are in Venice, Geneva, or Barcelona, but you only have to step out on to the balcony to greet the azure Aegean.

Sula informs me of my itinerary. Four hours from Thessalonika by car to Uranopolis, then three hours by sea to Daphne, the port of Athos. Tomorrow I will receive the permits. I ask her, "Are there anchorites?"

She smiles at me and doesn't understand.

"There have never been any. Women are not allowed there. Forty years ago a French writer, Maryse Choisy, managed to sneak in, after which she published a book. They say she had her breasts removed in order to disguise herself as a man, but she denied this later. Much earlier an Englishwoman visited there, Lady Stratford of Redcliffe."

There have been very few women on Mount Athos. In the fifth century, the Empress Pulcheria founded the monastery of Vatopedi. Much later the queen of Serbia came with her husband on pilgrimage. Respectful, the Turkish governors left their harems behind in Constantinople whenever they came to visit. Much earlier in the year 1200, the mountain was shaken by a great scandal. At that time, shepherds were allowed to keep their flocks on the mountain slopes. Then one day it was discovered that these shepherds were furnishing the monasteries with milk, wool, and their daughters. They were chased out, but along with them went half the monks. Thus the edict of Constantine Monomachus established in 1060 is still in force, which bans the entrance of every female animal, every woman, every eunuch, young boy, or unshaven male face, so I will let my beard grow. In the meantime I will prepare my suitcase with everything that might come in handy on Athos, that is in the year 1000: clothes, shoes, food, a complete survival kit.

Sula informs me that a photographer will accompany me. His name is David. He is Jewish and knows the mountain very well. He speaks several languages. I have hired him in order to keep my promise to the director: to furnish photos.

He speaks several languages but badly. He is Jewish but no one would ever know. He has red hair and tiny eyes, and very heavy, puffy lids. Everyone who has ever visited Israel indeed must wonder if the Jewish race really exists. I have met black Jews and Mongolian ones. Different races exist among dogs. A basset hound cannot mate with a Great Dane. But love melts the races and mixes them together. Even the monks of Mount Athos mixed with mountain shepherdesses.

David is forty years old. At first meeting, he is no charming fellow. He comes over to the car loaded down with his camera equipment, a couple of bags slung across his shoulder and a hunter's cap on his head. He dumps everything on the back seat next to me and climbs in next to the driver whose name is Demostenes. They speak and laugh without turning around. I am glad to avoid useless conversation which only wastes my energies without recharging me.

David turns around, his forehead is carved in wrinkles, his eyelids puffy, making him look much older than he really is. Sula must have told him about my journey in search of entronauts and now he wants to know what I think about India: Veda, the Upanishads, yoga, Tantra. Everything. His erudition surprises me, as much as his rudeness. I smile and try to avoid the question.

"Are there still hermits on Mount Athos?"

He frowns and asks brusquely, "Have you ever read Abulaphia?"

He turns back around and we drive through the forests along the coast. Silence until we reach Stagiras unexpectedly. I would like to get out here. This is Aristotle's birthplace, but I only find a small village, an ancient wall, a modern statue. Caper bushes are flourishing in the one-thousand-year-old wall.

However do they manage to find water with their roots clutching the stones, their leaves under the burning sun? Let's go. Anyway, Aristotle I never liked you much, enchanted as you were with your own reasons and unfaithful to Plato.

We drive on. David and Demostenes are chatting away. I pick up a few fragments: *ne, ochi, parakalo, efharisto*. These few words along with *Kalimera* and *Kalispera* are all I know of Greek, the language of Mount Athos. I must improve my relationship with David. But who is Abulaphia?

We drive on but the road grows worse and worse. At the beginning it was wide, smooth, and paved in asphalt, then it became a gravel road, and then a narrow dusty track full of holes, and now a trail winding in among streams and sand. If it goes on like this for much more, we'll have to stop and turn back.

Somehow we reach Trypiti: six small houses and a tiny port. Here we were to take the boat to Mount Athos, but the fishermen inform us that the boat has already left. There will be another one tomorrow. I get out. Here the peninsula of Athos begins. It is the closest point between two gulfs, about 2,000 metres across. On this isthmus Xerxes opened a canal to save his fleet five centuries before Christ. The emperor feared that the sudden storms so dangerous near the Mount might cause a disaster like the one which had just happened to Mardonius, who watched as his fleet of three hundred ships and his 20,000 soldiers were dashed upon the rocks. For months armed cadavers were washed up on the shore. Men have feared this sea for its sudden storms for thousands of years. Tomorrow I will cross it in a boat.

"How big is the boat?"

They show me one: eight metres long, two metres

wide, a diesel engine. Take care of this, Archangel, thanks.

We proceed on, tossing about in the car until we reach Uranopolis where the last trace of the road dies. Here the Byzantine emperor built a castle for his empress while he devoted himself to the spiritual life. Today, amid the ruins stand four houses, and a motel near the port. Demostenes unloads us along with all our equipment outside the motel. He says goodbye and rushes back to Thessalonika.

Here I am alone with David, so hostile. What have I done to him? We'll have to share the same experiences, crossing the sea, going up the mountain. We will have to work together to take photos. I try to be kind and help him with his bags, after picking up my own survival kit. But he doesn't thank me, and doesn't even look at me. He is one of those people who are born rude. I am incapable of dealing with him. I retreat, like a defenceless snail.

At the hotel, we are welcomed by a thin pale girl who speaks Italian. She studied in Perugia. She suggests that we have lunch and then go down to the dock. There we will most certainly find a boat to take us to the Mount today. It will cost one hundred drachmas. She says to us, "Eat now because on the mountain you won't get much to eat."

The restaurant is good, the fish very fresh and retsina reminds me of the Plaka. I pour David a few generous glasses of wine as an antidote to his sour mood. After the third glass, he smiles and a timid expression appears on his face which would have been unimaginable before.

"Did they tell you I am Jewish?"

"I have a few Jewish friends, and a great master, Bergson."

"You should read Abulaphia."

I pour him out a fourth glass and he takes me into his confidence. He was born in Thessalonika where his family had fled from Spain in 1492. For us that date signifies the discovery of America, but for the Jews, it marks the beginning of a great persecution.

"As a child I believed I was Greek. At ten I discovered I wasn't, and that I was Jewish. There were many of us in Thessalonika, now there are hardly any Jews left at all. We were of Spanish blood. Our women with their gypsyish coloured skirts, their hair tied up in ribbons, the curses of Cervantes in their mouths, are all gone now. I was the smallest of a large family: father, mother, brothers, sisters. A very large family. Whatever money was earned went into a drawer that was always kept unlocked. Whoever needed it could take from it. When I was ten the panzers arrived. I was down at the port when they first came. That evening when I went home, I found no one there. I called and called, but no one answered. They were all gone and they never came back. I never saw any of them again. Wiped out, non-existent, only a memory. I was ten years old." He falls silent and drains his glass. I look him in his tiny, heavy-lidded eyes. Those Spaniards in 1492 and those Germans in 1942 were all Christians, baptized. I am ashamed.

We have hired a motorboat which the fisherman guides slowly across a smooth sea, beneath a vibrant sun glittering in the water. The rhythm of the motor is slow, like the rocking of a cradle.

I have left everything in Uranopolis. When David saw my survival kit he asked me whether I intended to carry it on my back all the way up to Karyai – all the way up to an altitude of one thousand metres?

Aren't there any mules?

No mules until we have been given permission -and the permits are issued in Karyai. In that case the best thing to do was to leave everything at the motel. We brought only our camera equipment with us. I left everything: clothes, shoes, and food, my entire survival kit. Now naked, I put myself in the hands of the Archangel. It was like re-experiencing my marvellous pilgrimage with Kapila.

We left the little port of Uranopolis, the last of the profane ground. We followed the coast of the sacred peninsula covered with dense, savage forest, unchanged throughout time. There are no roads through those forests. We went back in time to the year 1000.

Athos is the name of a Titan in Hellenic mythology. He battled against Poseidon, who was one of the three faces of God, the others being Zeus and Hades. Man, when he confronts the gods, becomes a giant, or an angel like Jacob in the Bible who struggled with his angel for a whole night. The myth of the titan had many devoted followers who left Greece to settle on the mountain, giving it the name of Athos. After centuries and centuries gentle Christians joined those hermits. Perhaps the spirit of the mountain never noticed that its hermits had changed religion.

A few buildings appear amid the forests, but no human form, or voice. The rhythm of the motor seems to be lost in the huge silence.

In the midst of this great calm, I notice the fins of three sharks following us. I am horrified, but the fisherman is indifferent. He tells us a story about how three sharks devoured a novice from one of the monasteries. In order to capture them, the monks threw a sheep into the sea as bait. When they slit open the shark's belly, they found the sheep and the novice. David adds that these forests are inhabited by packs of wild wolves, savage boars, serpents, scorpions, and salamanders, and at two thousand metres, on the peak of Mount Athos, nests the royal eagle.

I ask when the novice died.

"Two hundred years ago."

We hug the sacred coastline, moving from monastery to monastery – which are sometimes located close to shore, or midway up the slope, or on the mountain peak.

Sometimes they appear suddenly among the trees, isolated, high on the cliff, with no road of access. David wants to show me the mountain before we begin our ascent on foot.

The fisherman dozes off and the sea shatters into glittering sparks. The fisherman is deep asleep, rocked by the rhythm of the motor.

Suddenly a citadel rises on the bank. The lower strata are gloomy and grey but above it is decked with innumerable balconies sustained by very slender wooden poles. Incredible. Our boat advances: a square tower appears, a Turkish clock tower. Then a vermilion church amid the medieval grey. It is the monastery of San Dionysius, six centuries old. It is not a monastery, but a curious colossus freed from the clutches of the mountain, smiling at the sea.

The vision disappears behind us and then an even more incredible sight comes into view: a huge castle enclosed within a curved, dentated wall. A pink wall, which surrounds the pink castle and a pink tower. Below a cascade of white rock about to tumble down, a dry river, undulating stones on a crumbling cliff. Everything is immobile through supernatural command, a miracle that cannot last. If even one stone should be removed, the whole thing would collapse. The pink wall, the pink tower, the castle have all been balanced there in perfect equilibrium for the last ten centuries. It is the monastery of St. Paul. Behind it, the peak of Mount Athos, a marble-green pyramid stark against the blue sky. Frowning, powerful, awesome Athos, a Titan rising against Poseidon.

David gives the order to head for the shore and the fisherman sits up, turns off the motor, and guides us slowly in. We had grown so accustomed to the churning of the motor that now the silence is most evident – absolute, unique. We disembark on Mount Athos.

The face of Dostoevsky. We have landed near the Russian monastery of Saint Panteleimon. At the entrance the guard, an elderly monk, is sitting on a bench, with three cats at his feet. Like all monks on Mount Athos he is dressed in an ankle-length tunic tied at the waist by a leather belt, and a cylindrical hat to keep his long hair out of his eyes. Like the holy men of India, they never cut their hair or shave their beards. The tunic and cylinder are black, stained, worn. His clothes must be at least seventy years old, like the monk himself. He is Russian and doesn't speak much Greek. He has the face of Dostoevsky, protruding cheekbones and a snub nose, glassy eyes turned towards another world.

David explains that we are on our way to Karyai, the capital, to obtain our permits. There on the Mount, every monastery offers food and lodging to the pilgrim if he is guaranteed permission by Karyai. The guard shrugs his shoulders. He could not care less about Karyai. If we want to stay at Saint Panteleimon, we are welcome. He rises to his feet with some difficulty, his ancient legs unsteady, and asks us to follow him. The cats precede us.

The Russian bell tower, globed and green, marks the hour in the monastery. Each monastery has its own time. Some begin calculating it at sunset, others at sunrise. As for the calendar, the mountain has its very own. Here time follows a circular path, not a straight line.

We follow the guardian and the jangling of his keys down along corridors which vanish into the darkness. We meet a few old monks, all Mongols, except for a couple of young, giant, blond monks. Saint Panteleimon has been languishing ever since St. Petersburg became Leningrad.

We go into a room. Inside it is 1910. On the walls large portraits of the Czar, the Czarina, the imperial family. Photographs dated 1905, a diploma from the year 1900. A lay brother welcomes us with the traditional refreshment for pilgrims: two small cups of Turkish coffee, water, a little plate of quince *glyco*, and tiny glasses of ouzo. I think it is rosolio and nearly gulp it down, but I stop myself in time. It is brandy, and powerful stuff. The water barely soothes the fire.

David, the interpreter, asks the old man, "Where are the hermits?"

"Hermitage? There are many hermitages on the mountain. Twenty monasteries and ten hermitages. 2,000 monks in all."

"And the anchorites?"

No. Hermitages are one thing – in Greek they are called *skiti*, but anchorites are something else again: men who live in forests and caves.

"Are you interested in Byzantine art or history?"

"No, I am looking for the anchorites."

"Do they still exist? I don't know. I have not left this place in ten years. They live in inaccessible places and are not accustomed to speaking to other people. They have been in isolation for years and years. Why do you want to meet them?"

His glassy eyes which seemed at first to be fixed on the other world now gaze down at me. I do not answer. It is too difficult to give him a thorough explanation.

"Don't you think there might be at least ten or so left?"

He looks at our camera equipment and asks suspiciously, "Do you work for a newspaper?"

"I want evidence of their existence."

The lay brother comes to take the tray away. David goes out to photograph the monastery – to do so he needs a double permit from Karyai: one issued by the ecclesiastical authorities and the other by the Greek police. The old man shrugs his shoulders and David goes out.

We are alone. The old man's eyes have gone glassy again, fixed on the other world. He mumbles in Russian, then picks up a piece of paper and scribbles a few signs. He pushes the note into my hand secretly as he gets up. The three cats run out from under the table.

David returns and asks me, "Shall we sleep here?"

"No, let's go. On to Karyai."

They told us it would take us two hours to get there, at the most two and a half. We have been walking now for four hours, making our way through the woods which grow thicker and thicker, along trails which grow narrower and narrower, without once encountering a sign, a monk, or another human being. We stop to rest in a clearing and put down our equipment which has become so heavy that we cannot carry it any longer. We are tired, cold, thirsty, and hungry. Low rain clouds are gathering overhead. It's twilight. At sunset the monasteries close up their doors and open them again at dawn.

David finds a tree with some berries that I have never seen before and we eat some, though they are unripe. We set out again. When we reach the top of this 1,000 metre peak we ought to be able to see something. We have a map of the peninsula, but we are so lost that it is of no use.

When we reach the top it is almost dark. On the other side of the mountain the woods stretch on and on. In the distance a light is burning. To the left I can distinguish the outline of a monastery. I head towards it, but David stops me. It is useless. The doors will be closed until dawn and we have no permit. Better not go. I look at him, poor Jew terrified by centuries of Christianity. I leave him behind. Let him wait for me. I'll pound on the door until I break it down if I have to I am resolute, a tenacious Lombard, a free spirit who has no intention of dying in the forest in the night, prey to wolves, boars, serpents, salamanders, owls, and the royal eagle.

I advance towards the monastery. Tall, Byzantine, purplish in the darkness. There is no light, no sound. I find the path and go to the entrance. It is open, as are all the windows, the doors, even the roof. It is a ruin, a marvellous ruin destroyed by a fire centuries ago. Only the outer shell is left. Now the tenacious Lombard in me relinquishes power and I cling to the Archangel and thank him because he has saved me, although at this moment all seems to be lost.

I find David sitting on the ground in the middle of his equipment. He has lit an electric torch. He questions me with his eyes, his lids so puffy he can barely keep them open, his forehead wrinkled into a frown.

I command, "Let's head for that light."

We start down the slope. There is a hut and light is filtering under the door. We hear youthful voices inside. I knock and three monks appear. Their bearded faces are consoling. In the forest, the presence of man is comforting. They show David the trail which will lead us to Karyai in five minutes.

Indeed it only takes us five minutes to get there. It is night and the streets are dark. So this is the capital? Rather, it is an ugly mountain village. A passer-by shows us the way to the Greek police station. Without a permit, we will find no place to sleep for the night. We go up the dark stairs to the guard post lit by the light of a kerosine lantern. We give the official our papers. I sit on the couch and doze off while David explains. Then he calls me, and the guard gives us our papers. The stairway is even darker on the way down. Outside, the cobbled streets are slick with rain. We are hungry, tired, and thirsty. We find the inn where one can have a meal, but it is closed. We knock and someone appears. Yes, you may eat, there is a dormitory. Just like in the year 1000. Under the light of a kerosine lamp, half asleep, I consume our meal of beans, tomatoes, black bread and water. Then I grope my way to the stinking medieval latrine.

Forty years ago an Englishman wrote that he had killed ninety-six red bedbugs here in one night and that he was disappointed not to have killed one hundred. Perhaps I will win the prize? I keep my eyes tightly closed while I remove my shoes. DDT, genocide of bedbugs. Perhaps DDT has finally found its way back to the year 1000. I blow out the lantern. David's lantern is already out. This mattress is much harder than the inflatable one I had in India,but much better than wild animals, basilisks, wolves, and so on.

On the scrap of paper that the old Russian monk gave me, three words have been written in an unsteady hand: "Panta" or "Panto", "Krates" or "Kratoros" and "Karoulia". Greek is a difficult language. The vowel "i" can be expressed by means of seven different signs. "Panta" means everything, "Krates" means sir, and "Karoulia" pulley.

David is unable to make anything of it either, and anyway he is too busy rushing around to see about our permits. Karyai may be the capital but it is really a village, with small shops selling food and rosaries, a tiny post office, taverns with rooms and stables. Very few lay brothers walk these disconnected streets: a few Greek pilgrims, German students, a couple of professors and merchants. However, it is full of monks: the shopkeepers, shoppers, and muleteers. Monks of all ages and all kinds, dressed in silk with bushy patriarchal beards, with soft hands that the people in the street stop to kiss, wandering monks dressed in rags, vagabond monks filthy and deformed, smiling youths fresh from the seminary, the first hairs sprouting amid their acne, dreamy monks tripping on the cobblestones.

Silk or rags, fat or thin. Injustice even on Mount Athos. The same human injustices even here, like everywhere else in the world. I smile bitterly, but is my bitterness real? If I am sincere, I must realize that it is not. It is a smile of self-satisfaction, of "I told you so". My successful prediction makes me feel smug. To our minds it is an injustice. We want to be rich men and not beggars. But what about them? They have chosen extreme poverty. They have chosen it for practical reasons. The path of inner life is a complex reality and only the traveller knows what is best for him. Only the traveller knows the peace, serenity, gaiety, perfection, and mystery of the superhuman encounter. To those same entronauts our life seems infernal, mad, and the condition of the wealthy horrifies them. The wealthy man passes by in the streets of Karyai and the beggar looks at him in pity.

The whole hierarchy passes by in the streets of Karyai, which indeed represents the history of the mountain. The hierarchy begins at the top, at the peak, when the mountain first offered its hospitality only to the anchorites. Later came the wandering ascetics who lived by begging, and later on, a bit lower on the slopes a few hermits established themselves in groups of two or three. A little bit lower the coenobia were formed. Then three centuries ago, the lowest rungs were created. A few monasteries, lacking funds, allowed the development of private enterprise, so that in the same monastery some had more, others had less. Today, all these different forms of inner search still co-exist, all legitimate because the hierarchical descent has not threatened the top, where the anchorites are. If they are gone, then Athos is a dead mountain.

On the streets of Karyai you may meet the holy, the rich, the poor, the illiterate, the bookish, the fervent and the gentle, the active and the ecstatic, those who stink and are proud of it, others as perfumed as angels. I pass by Saint Bernard, Saint Labre, Saint Benedict, Saint Bruno, Saint Louis, Saint Francis with Orthodox names.

Yet all the same I feel that something is missing here in Karyai, but I cannot define the uneasiness I feel. I have seen villages much worse than this where the shops were dustier, the tavern more squalid, and the rooms untidier. Why is it that Karyai, the capital of peace, resembles a barracks? That's it, now I know what is missing: women, their voices, their feminine delicacy and presence, and the shouting of children.

David returns to the inn, authorized with all the necessary permits. He introduces me to Anghelos, a lay muleteer, who has the face of a highwayman. With his pack animals he will lead us wherever we wish. He has been a muleteer on Athos for twenty years and has a wife and children in Trypiti. After having transported so many German professors in search of Byzantine art, he has even learned a few words of German. He understands immediately who is paying and ignores David, who engaged him, and only addresses me, with his one-hundred-word vocabulary. He is a sly fox.

"I'm looking for the anchorites."

"Anchorites? Finished. Once down here desert. Now finished. Desert, not mule track. Anchorites finished."

Anchorites finished? That means mountain finished, religion finished. You have let the last Christian anchorite die, the last of a hundred generations and you do not even realize it and you did not even weep. If it is true that the opening between sky and earth has closed up again, then there is no remedy for our egoism. For the joy which trickles through that opening is the only thing that can destroy our selfishness. If the opening has closed, we must dwell in desperation until another one is opened.

I show him the note, still undecoded, written by the Russian monk.

He reads it and understands immediately.

"Pantocrator. Monastery. East. Karoulia. *Skiti*. South. Beneath the cliff Athos. Desert near. Journey three days. Visit monastery four days."

"Great Lavra *skiti* Saint Anna, five days. Three mules. 3,000 drachmas." He is a highwayman. David asks if the itinerary is all right with me. My last hope is in this scrap of paper. Is it all right? Perhaps. They begin bartering in Greek, the Jew and the highwayman and, for this purpose, they obtain some beer and cigarettes from the tavern keeper. Five days, three mules, and 2,900 drachmas. Please, enough. When are we leaving? My mule is a little horse of great merit, as Anghelos assures me. The only thing I've ridden on in my life is a bicycle. Our caravan sets out, with David on a mule at the front, me in the middle with my little horse, and Anghelos on a mule at the rear with our photographic equipment and some provisions. We soon leave Karyai behind us and venture into the forest along narrow trails which intersect each other, all identical. Only Anghelos can tell which way to go, and from the rear he shouts to tell the first mule when it's time to turn. The mule understands.

Now I know how people lived during the year 1000. The earth was covered with forests. Man crossed them in solitude, meditating in silence. The forest nourished him with its fruit and game, he drank from streams, warmed himself with wood, healed himself with herbs, and built a hut for himself out of tree trunks. In the forest you observe the ground and recognize the ferns, the moss, the oaks, the chestnuts. You observe the sky, predict the winds, the clouds, the rain and sunshine. The forest teems with animals. They are all around you. Squirrels pouncing, snakes slithering in the grass, hares leaping. The whistle of the wood-chuck, the song of the birds, the gentle eyes of the buck, the galloping of the deer, the howling of the wolf. The forest sometimes opens out onto vast meadows where the grass grows so tall you are lost in it. Sometimes the woods are dark and silent amid high conifers, a cathedral in which a solemn and mysterious presence descends upon you. The men who lived in the year 1000 knew things of which we are ignorant.

When a cold wind begins blowing and night is falling, Anghelos shouts at the animals to hurry them on towards the monastery, the only place we may find food and lodging for the night. It is the monastery of Pantocrator, the double word which the Russian monk wrote in his mysterious note.

We are welcomed once again with Turkish coffee, water, ouzo, *glyco*. David chats with the guard, Anghelos disappears into the barn. A monk peers out at us. I go into the church which is very dark, full of thick clouds of incense. The monks are singing the Orthodox liturgy in grave voices. I go out again, and a little monk approaches me – the ivory pallor of his face enhanced by his black robes. It is Father Basilio, one of the few monks who is also a priest. He speaks Italian. He immediately offers to show me around the library. He thinks I'm interested in Byzantine art. I disappoint him by asking if I may put off the visit until the next day, as my legs are aching from the ride and I can barely stand up.

I find David in the ancient kitchen. Two monks are serving the food: beans, tomatoes, black bread, and water. We go out to look at the sunset. I feel a deep nostalgia for the Indian sunset, for Kapila. The monastery is built on a rock facing the sea. This is the astonishing moment when the sun sinks into the Mediterranean and launches a green ray just before it disappears, which very few people manage to see. Those who glimpse the green ray this evening are promised a great day tomorrow.

David and I are there ready to seize it, the fishers of a ray which perhaps is only in our imagination. No, there it is, real: a green flash. We begin to laugh and pat each other on the back. We have become friends. He repeats to me:

"Do you know Abulaphia? No? What a shame. And the Cabbala? Don't you even know that the Cabbala interprets the Bible with *Gigul* or metempsychosis?

No? That's a shame. You went all the way to India, all the way back to the year 1000 to search for non-existent entronauts and you never noticed the Jews you had near you."

I feel he is offended and try to justify myself. I did what I could. I met a few people, and by no means not everyone. I neglected Black Africa, for example, and the descendants of the Mayas and the Incas, who continue their traditions. I have many reasons to reproach myself, and many reproach me, both Catholics and Protestants. I have not sought the disciples of St. John of the Cross, nor of Niccolo della Flue, nor George Fox. Do they still exist? I have not sought the Jewish cabbalists. I went where the wind blew me, and there is always a wind blowing me somewhere. I'm sorry, David. Tell me about Abulaphia.

Now I realize that his tiny eyes behind those puffy lids are really gentle. He has been wounded, it is most evident, and his rudeness protects his scars. He has forgiven me. He takes a little book out of his pocket, goes over to the lantern in the dormitory where we are alone, and begins reading aloud from Abulaphia, the medieval master born in Saragossa.

"O Israelite, get ye ready. Find a solitary place where no one may hear your voice. Sit in your room and reveal the secret to no man. Purify your body, purify your mind. You will need a strong body, a clear spirit, and an open mind. You are about to unleash an impetuous torrent, and if you are unprepared, you will drown. Pray, meditate, assume the posture I have indicated, breathe with the rhythm I have given you. Proceed slowly: months, years, decades. You have all eternity before you. In time thoughts will come without words, in time a silence will come in which you cannot speak. Be calm if you are shaken by a great trembling: it is the soul which wishes to flee from its vehicle. One day while I sat writing I suddenly saw my shape, separate from me. If this should happen, you should know that it is like choosing death. Then return to your body and its needs. Get up, drink, eat, refresh yourself with a pleasant perfume. By now your spirit is unsealed. Divine life is about to burst out into your soul. One day you will be filled by a jubilant joy that I cannot describe. You will have found Eden."

David is silent. The path to Eden is always the same, only the name changes. Eden – a place existing nowhere, outside of time, elusive. But man must maintain his bridge to joy if he does not wish to perish. This is the function of the entronauts.

Today will be a great day, if the green ray has told the truth. Father Basilio takes me to the library. He is so eager that I do not dare confess my indifference. He shows me illuminated manuscripts number 49 and 61, both dating from the eleventh century. Out of cowardice, I try to fake an admiration which I do not feel. Nor do I feel it for Silvio Pellico, *Le mie prigioni*, 1847. But when my eyes fall upon the first edition of the *Philokalia*, Venice 1782, and *Invisible Struggle*, Venice 1796, I let out a cry. These are the two major texts of Byzantine hesychasm, a form of Christian entronautics. Father Basilio, bibliophile, beams.

"Are you interested in the hesychasts?"

Am I interested in them? I have journeyed all the way around them in my slow readings. Saint Simeon in the year 950: "Close the door of your room, sit in a corner and raise your mind above the useless and transient things. Lay your beard on your breast, fix your eyes upon your umbilical region, slow your breath and search for your heart in the centre of the soul. At first everything will seem dark and uncomfortable to you. Persevere. A moment will suddenly come in which an immense light will appear and you will discover an inexpressible joy." It sounds like Abulaphia, and all the others.

"Are you interested in hesychasm?"

Am I interested? I have navigated round it in my slow reflections. We men are often willing to make great efforts, tolerate discomfort, illness, danger and go to great expense to enjoy a moment of love which is frequently brief, disappointing, and preceded by complicated rituals – and yet if we are willing to modify our whole life for this fleeting pleasure, how is it that we cannot understand the entronauts who seek and find a joy far more intense and lasting? These are not sentimental chimeras but a joy far more real than our brief sexual union.

Seeing that I have remained silent, Father Basilio repeats the question, "Are you interested in hesychasm?"

At my nod, he lifts a cloth covering one of the glass cases and shows me the library's entire collection of hesychastic texts (dating back to its earliest infancy, to the most ancient manuscripts) from the fifth century to the death of Saint Seraphim in 1833.

Basilio remarks: "This monastery, Pantokratoros has always been the centre of the hesychasts. Here the *Philokalia* was written, and here we have the original *The Way of a Pilgrim*. Here Byzantine hesychasm was born . . . "

I reply unkindly, "And you let it die here?"

He looks at me shocked, as if I have accused him of murder. He is about to answer, but he swallows his words. Silently he replaces the cloth. At that moment a monk with white hair and beard and a dignified bearing appears in the doorway. Basilio goes to him and kisses his hand. The old man interrogates me with his eyes, the little monk whispers an explanation. He must be the Prior. He comes over to me, and asks me to sit down. He wants to know where I am from and why I have come. He has a natural yet kindly air of authority about him.

"You have been in Siam? Good. You have been in India? Good. Interested in hesychasm? Good."

"Yes, hesychasm. What year did it die?"

For a minute his eyes burn through me, but his face does not change beneath his bushy white beard. He gets up and pronounces, "As long as the mountain lives, hesychasm will live."

I want to answer, "And vice versa."

Instead, I am silent, because the Prior's words have given me new hopes. Father Basilio accompanies him. The old man pauses in the doorway and looks at me, and then gives an order to the little monk – who listens reverently. Is the Prior telling him to chase me out? He goes out and Basilio runs over to me.

"He has told me to take you this afternoon to see Macarius, a saint."

"Is he alive?"

"Yes, he is a living hesychast."

Yet ten of them were required to save Sodom and Gomorrah.

We should have brought two mules, for the road is very long. but I am the only one who has received permission for this visit. David and Anghelos are excluded, and thus the mules as well. The road is long and steep. Father Basilio, though pale, is quite quick. He runs along ahead of me, boasting in silence of his agility while I stubbornly follow, panting and dripping sweat. But my pride isn't enough to help me keep up with him, so he stops and waits for me and we continue up at my pace. He tells me about the saint.

Macarius came to Athos twenty years ago. Now he must be about forty. He was born near Thessalonika, and he was a longshoreman. He asked if he could live in the forest, where he met another very old hermit, a hesychast master, who has been dead for many years. A longshoreman? It must be a trade which leads to wisdom. Ammonius, the famous master of the Christian Origen and the pagan Plotinus, unloaded sacks in the port of Alexandria.

Macarius built himself a hut in a tree out of branches. He doesn't always come down from his tree, rarely speaks, often sings and sometimes disappears. Animals gather round him without fear. In the winter the monastery sends him a bit of food. In the other seasons, he eats whatever he can find in the forest. He is a monologist hesychast, night and day he breathes the word "Jesus" in his heart. His presence in the forest is a very well-kept secret. I have had great luck – something in me must have convinced the Prior. Father Basilio stares at me, wondering what it might have been that persuaded him. He must find nothing because he adds, "Macarius is not a saint because he lives this way. He is a saint because he is a saint. Have you ever seen a saint?"

He is worried. He considers me disrespectful. He is afraid that I might confuse sainthood with madness. He is afraid of that western good sense which would put penicillin on the stigmata of Francis of Assisi or lock Niccolo della Flue away in a madhouse. No, Father Basilio, I have never seen a saint. The men I have searched for across the continents are called sages, victors, free men, enlightened, blessed, perfect. David calls them prophets, though I call them entronauts.

Kapila is an entronaut, a Tantric master. I have come to Athos to find saints, but what does the name matter, if they all meet in Eden?

The forest has grown dark and thick. The trail has vanished. I follow Basilio silently. Suddenly a dog barks. Dogs bark to defend the place where man is. If they have gone wild, they do not bark.

A big dog suddenly appears among the trees and faces us – ears pricked up, tail in the wind, teeth bared. He reminds me of the mongrels in Benares, but he is not trembling, rather he is quite hostile. Basilio stops and calls.

"Macarius, Macarius."

The dog sniffs his robes, wags his tail in recognition, and leads us to a little clearing where I glimpse the anchorite. He approaches us. He is a tall, thin man, but not emaciated. He is wearing a tattered Orthodox robe, and is naked underneath. He has a great mass of curly hair, black like his beard. A youthful face amid the whiskers. His eyes are large, long, and luminous. I recognize them immediately – Kapila's eyes, the gentleness in his gaze finds its way to your breast and melts your heart. He does not speak but nods to us, indicating that we should sit down on a tree trunk.

We obey. He goes away and returns with two large leaves filled with wild fruit and two hollowed pine cones filled with spring water. This is his offering to visitors. He gestures to us to drink and eat. He shows us his mouth, to indicate that he is unable to speak. He begs us to be patient. His hands are very eloquent.

He is sitting on the ground under the tree where his hut is built. The dog lies down next to him. The birds begin singing again. A few perch on his shoulders. Kapila, the Tantric master, Kapila of the squirrels.

With much difficulty, he begins to speak and

excuses himself with a smile which makes him seem very youthful.

"I'm losing the power of speech. It takes me a while to come down."

Basilio becomes my interpreter and tells him about the Prior and myself. Macarius turns to me.

"What can I do for you?"

Face to face with the entronauts, I do not know what to say. I only want to ask their blessing. I would have too many things to say. I want to tell him about the 12th of April in Mahabalipur. I want to tell him of my return to Europe, of my loss of serenity and joy. To tell him about the frenetic vibrations which I cannot bear. Tell him about my perverse cohabitant and his demoralizing secrets. But how can I tell him all this, here in this place, in this green and quiet forest, far from the world. How can I tell this man who dwells on an island of heroes, who can barely talk?

My discouragement must have shown in my face, or perhaps he understood intuitively the things I did not say, or perhaps seen from his dimension, I was an open book. He murmurs with difficulty – "The great ascetic does not live in the forest, but among the people" – unaware that he was merely repeating something a Sufi had once told me.

"Macarius, who isn't a great ascetic, or even a little one? How can one manage among people?"

"What is your profession?"

"I write."

"Good. Listen. I lived among people – it was like forgetting myself, losing myself constantly. The only real sin is forgetting oneself. But there is a remedy."

"A remedy for forgetting oneself?"

"Yes. Do your part, play your role. My role wants me to be an anchorite and yours a writer. Write, do your best, but do not worry about the result. Let Him have the result you work to obtain His aims. Is the result a great success? Good. Is it a great failure? Good. Riches? Good. Poverty? Good. It doesn't concern us. If we free ourselves from the obsession of the result, if we pluck it out by the roots, we are safe. Then work for Him, for the ever-present one, for His joy, you understand."

"That joy?"

"Yes, but first you must pull out the last root. Tear it out."

He uproots a weed.

"Like that."

I repeat, "But people? You don't know what people are like. Women entice you, men attack you. You must always be bothering about them, worrying about whether they will say yes or no, and you become frenetic and desperate."

"There is a remedy. Look at them in the pupils. Not in the eyes, but the pupils. If you look close you will see the soul in the pupil. Try it, and you'll see. If you look at the soul, you will encounter the presence, the same presence in everyone, you will find it everywhere and the frenzy will vanish. Don't you believe me? Try it. The frenzy ends and brotherhood begins."

As he said goodbye to us, he repeated, "These are two great remedies. Try them."

I look into his pupils and find a living presence. His pupils can see far away, they see the Eden of my nostalgia.

The dog accompanies us for part of the way, wagging his tail.

After Pantocrator we headed towards Karoulia. The old Russian monk had told the truth. Anghelos and his mules carry us through the great forests, the vast olive groves, among towering cypresses. David and his equipment capture faces, expressions, places. We woke at dawn and were ready to sleep at dusk. We ate beans, tomatoes, black bread and water. The hardness of our straw mattresses did not keep us from sleeping like logs. It was impossible to wash or to shave – we could only freshen our eyes at dawn in the courtyard fountains. I remember one splendid fountain with ten animals vomiting water, and below two smiling Chinese dogs.

We stopped at every monastery, and at every *skiti*. Great Lavra, the main monastery, the most ancient, founded by the anchorite Athanasius who lived fifty years in a cave. Great Lavra, which was built on a temple of Minerva – a disordered and giant monastery, both a village and a fortress. Kiliandari, founded by a eunuch. Here a thousand monks were killed in the time of the iconoclasts. Caracalla, not the work of the emperor, but of a Turk by that name: often Arabs and Turks came here on pilgrimages and the sultans built monasteries. Not because they were tired of Mohammed, but because they knew that there was only one God and all roads lead to him. This is monotheism. The other form, which pretends that only one's own God is the true one, is merely idolatry.

Simon-Peter, the monastery built high on a precipice, identical to the Buddhist Patala in Tibet. Tibet and Athos, tiny republics run by monks. Vatopedi, a colourful place with a white bell tower, a church rusted red, and roofs yellow with lichen. Among its treasures are seventy portraits of Mary, believed to have been painted by Luke the evangelist.

You encounter Mary wherever you go on Mount Athos. She came here after the crucifixion and since then the mountain has been consecrated to her. She came here because it was here that Lucifer brought Jesus, here to the top of this mountain, to tempt him by offering him all the kingdoms of the earth. From the top you can see as far as Thessalonika and Constantinople. Here Mary left a piece of her camel-skin belt that she had made with her own hands, a precious relic of miraculous powers. I begin to think that here on Mount Athos, as in Tantrism, God is a feminine divinity.

We stop at every monastery, at every *skiti* where we find relics. Fragments of the True Cross, including the largest fragment in existence, thirty centimetres long. A tooth of Christopher, the saint who was born with a dog's head. As soon as he became a Christian, his head became human and was so beautiful that it converted fifty thousand women, including one hundred courtesans who had been sent to seduce him. The paten of Pulcheria which boils water without fire. And the most famous icon of the Orthodox world, painted one thousand years ago. In the midst of an Arab invasion, a monk grabbed it and threw it into a well, and didn't even have time to blow out the candle. When the Arabs had gone and the icon was removed from the well, the candle was still burning.

Legends and relics are the testimony of ancient thoughts and ancient feelings, deserving our respect because they have helped whole generations of humanity to elevate themselves. We no longer know how to use them. In analogy, imagine future generations forgetting how to operate our electric power houses, but dutifully conserving the ruins, in memory of a lost knowledge.

Then the monasteries end, along with the woods and

the paths. Before us only the expanse of rock where the animals cannot walk, because they might slip on the stone and fall over the edge. We must continue on foot and Anghelos takes his leave of us.

I have grown quite fond of my little horse – as attentive to my fear as I am to his hunger. Along the steepest precipices, he did not follow the mules along the edge, but kept close to the mountain, sparing me a few dizzy spells. In turn, I let him eat as much grass as he wished, ignoring the protesting Anghelos, who grew hostile whenever we slowed down. At the end of the day's journey, my little horse would rub his head against me, wanting a caress. Now I pat him for the last time while Anghelos says goodbye to us – adding stubbornly, "Anchorites finished".

Was Macarius the last one? Yet I trust in the words of the old monk: Karoulia.

To reach Karoulia, you must pass Katunakia, a hermitage for artists. It is a tranquil place on the sea, most privileged, where seven painters, all monks, continue the tradition of Byzantine painting, an art which has never sought harmony or sweetness, nor has ever tried to reproduce a figure or an object or a shape, but rather attempts to convey a message to the viewer. In this peaceful hermitage, Byzantine painting continues in a modern vein without changing the message.

These monks are smiling, friendly, very tall and robust, with long beards and flowing hair. They greet us warmly, offer us food and drink and show us their paintings, give us directions. I ask the question, "Are there anchorites in Karoulia?"

The youngest one with blond hair and rosy cheeks replies, "Yes, of course."

"How many are there?"

"I believe there must be about twenty-one, in the caves, the huts, and on the cliff."

I laugh, relieved.

"How do they live? And how can I reach them?"

They live by Divine Providence, which is a sort of hierarchy in which all things and all beings have a place, even finger nails and thoughts, microbes and archangels, men and stars. Providence has its bizarre twists – it sends a disciple of Abulaphia and of Kapila together to Mount Athos. It is not bizarre, but obvious and easy to understand. It is the providence of the anchorites. It begins with hunger and thirst. Especially with thirst, because if you do not have water to drink, you will die soon. Anchorites drink nothing but rain water and this is a place where long dry spells are not uncommon.

"And if it doesn't rain?"

They die. If your time has come, does it matter if you die of thirst or dropsy?

The blond reassures me, "But God sees all and provides for them."

"And how do they eat?"

"Thanks to Karoulia, that means 'the pulley'.

Karoulia is a desert, a vertical desert. Precipices three hundred metres down to the foaming and restless sea, an open sea where your eye may expand into the infinite and your soul may expand in astonishment. For twenty centuries this has been the chosen place of the great anchorites, exposed to all the elements – parching sun, whipping winds, freezing cold at night, and the salt sea air.

We left all our luggage at Katunakia. Karoulia is below us, there is no road down. Here the rocks end where we have destroyed our shoes and cut our feet, so unsuited even for mules, and in truth, unsuited to men.

Karoulia is below us, inaccessible, unless we use the ropes like rock climbers. David has brought only one camera with him, the most light-weight one. I look at him and tell myself that I cannot ask him to go down the rock face with me. He is a photographer from Thessalonika and has agreed to accompany me in exchange for meagre pay. But more than a photographer, he has been my guide and friend in an arduous journey. He has even confided to me the secrets of the cabbalists. He is a Jew. Why should he care about anchorites? He is not compelled by the same urgent feelings.

"David, I am going down alone."

Indignation lights up in those little eyes below their puffy lids. The disciple of Abulaphia replies, "You want to leave me now at this point?"

We begin the descent which is very easy at first, for we cling to the last trees growing in between the rocks. But soon we have to stop. There are no more trees to grab hold of. David finds the solution: footholds in the rock, centuries old, rusted, dubious. We go down. I squeeze my eyes shut to resist dizziness. How will we find our way back again?

There it is, down there along the steep cliffs the tiny huts made out of poles, branches, bricks, and laminated steel roofs. In the distance I can see the caves. Blank eyes stare out at the immense sea.

I stop in a clearing. The wind ruffles my hair and the sun burns my face. The only sound in that silence is the breaking of the waves. It is an astonishing moment of blinding light and colours. I stare at those huts and caves. An emotion wells up in my chest and renders me Christian. Are twenty-one anchorites enough to absolve the centuries of infamy and betrayal?

We continue down, grabbing on to some heavy iron

chains which perhaps were fastened to these rocks by some ancient anchorite, a blacksmith by trade. How will we get back?

Almost a path, more suited to goats if there were any. We follow, holding on to the rock, until the first hut appears. It must be the hut of Nicodemus who the painters told us about. Nicodemus is a Russian. He has been there for thirty-three years. He must be about eighty now. The blond painter warned us. "Be careful when you talk to him. He does anything you ask, including miracles."

We meet him in the doorway of his hut. In his long faded robe his lean body seems seven feet tall. He is straight and emaciated, his cheekbones seem to pierce through the skin, his eyes are tiny, pale blue, and childlike, his smile toothless. He speaks in Russian and David translates.

"Dear children, welcome, welcome. Come in, come in."

The shade of the hut is refreshing after the sun on the rocks, the effort, and the fear. There is so little space in the hut that the three of us barely fit inside. Three walls are made of planks, the fourth is rock, and the roof is laminated steel. There is no furniture except for a bench where he invites us sit. On the wall, a few old images glued to pieces of wood. I observe a faded archangel, a white horse, a fallen warrior with an evil face and red garments, pierced by the lance of the archangel who seems gentle despite his pose. A Cyrillic inscription and a date: 1884. The meaning is clear. There is a choice to make: the archangel or the dweller of the underground.

While our eyes grow accustomed to the light, Nicodemus brings in two bowls of water from a half-empty cistern. With a toothless smile he offers us his rain water, as precious to him as blood. I do not dare refuse, yet I do not dare drink it.

David asks him, "How do you eat?"

He would like to tell us something, but cannot find words, and only shrugs his shoulders. He has followed my eyes and now he removes the icon from the wall and hands it to me. It is old, faded, perhaps a gift from his mother in a Russian village, cherished throughout these long years of his existence, this long life of an entronaut.

I give it back to him. He takes it in his hands – large calloused hands, the hands of a peasant. He studies the image of the archangel, animated in his eyes by many memories and prayers.

He tells us that he is in the process of repairing his hut which is in bad shape, and that he received it from his master and that he must repair it because there is a young monk on the waiting list ready to take it over when he is gone.

I ask him, "Are you waiting for death?"

"Death? Death does not exist."

David photographs him and the hermit allows him to dictate any pose. He is childlike and innocent, oblivious to himself. I met a Kapila in wisdom and a Nicodemus in holiness.

When the moment comes to leave, he takes the archangel from the wall and hands it to me.

"Take it."

I would like to refuse, but I am touched by the gesture. He comes with us for a bit of the way and shows us the way down to the three monks who live below him. The others cannot be reached, they are isolated among the rocks.

David precedes me on the way down. I realize that he is now complaining about what I was complaining about before.

"How are we going to get back?"

The answer comes to my lips unexpectedly, a surprise even to myself, as if it were not my own.

"Why go back?"

The three anchorites are Seraphim of the pulley, Pakomio of the ecstasy and Philotheos of the cavern.

We find Seraphim in a clearing where a small white chapel stands which seems quite new. He does not notice us as he is busy working – applying plaster to the walls, singing.

He is a tiny man, more a worker than a monk. He is wearing what is left of a long tunic which is so torn that his arms, legs and the back of his wrinkled neck show through. Long beard and long hair in plaits.

David coughs and Seraphim turns around. He is not surprised, but smiles, then immediately feels embarrassed and runs away. He quickly returns in another robe, so faded and worn that it seems even more pitiful than the first. He apologizes and greets us.

"Christ is risen."

He takes us into the chapel, clean as a Dutch home. Embarrassed by our dirty shoes, we hurry out again. No no (he says) he did not build it, it is very old. He only looks after it. He defends it from the wind, the damp, and sun. No, no (he says) he doesn't sleep there, he sleeps outside under the tiny portico. The chapel is reserved for the anchorites whenever they come down or up for a visit. No no, he says, he is not an anchorite, he only takes care of the chapel.

David asks him, "What do you drink?"

He points to the sky, which is clear, without a cloud, without the slightest hope of rain.

"And how do you eat?"

He points at a pulley fastened to the edge of the cliff.

"You eat, drink, and sleep like an anchorite, therefore you must be one."

He considers this, then makes a grimace. He denies it. "No. No. They are anchorites, but I'm not."

He is a very cheerful fellow. When he isn't talking, he is singing. He takes us to see the pulley and shows us how it works, singing all the way. Every now and then he says to himself, suddenly lighting up, "Christ is risen".

The pulley is used to cast a rope down to the sea. At the end of the rope is a tiny basket so small that nothing bigger than a sandwich would fit inside. If a monk fisherman passes by there, if the season is good, if the stormy sea allows the boat to approach the rocks, and if the fisherman has some food, he puts it in the basket and Seraphim, when he notices, pulls it up again and shares the contents with the other three hermits. If God wishes.

I stare at him and he gives me the good news. "Christ is risen."

He adds. "Pakomio of the ecstasy is twenty metres below. Then turn left along the path and it will take you to the cavern of Philotheos. Then turn right and there's an iron ladder (be careful, three rungs are missing) and you'll find your way back to Katunakia."

Seraphim gives us his final advice, which is rather obscure. It is better to be silent with Pakomio who is hardly ever on earth, always in heaven. It is useless to visit Philotheos who is not in his cavern at the moment, but down on the rocks. Instead in the cave we will find Master Gregorio who lived there for fifty years and was the master of all three of them.

David asks doubtfully, "But how will we find him if he is dead?"

"His bones. They're very good for you." To get down to Pakomio there are no iron chains, but rather ropes with one end tied to the rock and the other dangling free. We brace our feet against the rock and slide down.

David complains, "How will we ever get back to Katunakia?

I have been enchanted by Nicodemus, by Seraphim, by Karoulia, by the sea, the sky, the rocks, the solitude, and the silence. It is the same enchantment that overwhelmed me in the Temple on the Shore, on the shores of the Indian Ocean. The same sense of having arrived. I repeat, astonished, "Why go back?"

Pakomio is sitting on the ground, his back resting against the wall of his fragile hut constructed out of a few poles, branches, and a metal roof. He is immobile and doesn't notice us. We cautiously walk around him. He is quite a big man compared to the other anchorites. A huge mass of hair and beard, never cut, hides his youthful face, which might be the face of a Greek statue. His eyelids are lowered, his face is serene. There is a faint smile on his lips, hermetic, inward. He is extraordinarily handsome.

The man who reaches the sublime, even in solitude, helps all men share in it, through a process of osmosis. He is only a great benefactor.

So then this is ecstasy. I stare at him, my feelings split between curiosity and reverence. He breathes faintly, his hands lying relaxed in his lap, his face alabaster, gold and luminous. This is ecstasy, the encounter between man and the divine. Ecstasy is the power of sabotage. The ecstasy of Saint Paul, Buddha, Plotinus, Ali, Lao Tse, Krishna, and of the many others who have changed the world. The ecstasy from which everything we posses derives and which elevates us. The ecstasy which frightens our tiny mind.

David is getting ready to take a photo and I become furious. I stop him and drag him away. Let's go, no more sacrilege. We walk towards the cavern of Philotheos. Dusk is falling.

I can see the cave in the distance: it is quite large. Similar in shape to an almond-shaped eye. Red rock, red ground, a harsh red. A green grassy spot nearby. We peek into the entrance. It is dark, shady, red, vast and secret. There is no one there. Philotheos is away, he has gone down to the rocks.

David complains. "May I take a photo?"

I go towards the green spot and nearly trip on a skeleton lying in the grass. It is a long red skeleton which has taken on the colour of the cave where it was buried. This is what is left of Master Gregorio, the anchorite who lived here for fifty years, a skull without a jaw bone.

I have fled the world to escape it and here it is. It has come to meet me. I have talked about it to everyone and now I see it. I talked about it with everyone, with Edoardo when he showed me my crocodile. On the nudist beach with the Irish setter girl, "I am a madman who doesn't want to die." To Ruzbehan, the Persian with the big nose, "Everyone accepts and yet everyone tries not to think about it. Everybody dies; not to die, that is the aim." After the 12th of April I didn't talk much about it. In that joy death seemed an absurdity. I had even forgotten it.

But it remembered me. Here it is, a skull in a grassy spot, with its sad sneer, telling me that there is no salvation, not even for those who have suffered fifty years in a cave. Contemplation of death, the exercise of an anchorite. In the Mediterranean sunset, the first stars appear.

I sit down on the ground next to the death and look at it. How can I flee from it if I carry it inside me, beneath my flesh, patiently waiting for me with this same sneer? I look at it and interrogate it. Only death can help us understand life.

It does not answer. Is this the silence of nothingness? Nothing does not exist, if it did, it would not be nothing. Is it the silence of the inferno? But hell does not exist, if it did God would be imperfect. Is it the silence of a secret? Is it the tacit invitation to search? Is it the encouragement to break with this tiny life to find a divine life? It is silent. Or it answers with my own mouth. Perhaps it is saying, you are born and die in the same place: in eternity.

I look up at a star. Perhaps it also died millions of years ago. But its life travels eternally in space and our eye encounters it alive. The star is not dead and does not die. What dies falls from life.

Sunset, the privileged hour. At the Temple on the Shore it was dawn. But here, again, the dam breaks and a vibrant stream of joy gushes forth within me. A secret soul opens inebriated by the nearness of the divine.

David calls, "Shall we start back?"

Go back? There he is, the Archangel.